CELL & MOLECULAR BIOLOGY

AN INTRODUCTION

SECOND EDITION
Revised Printing

Kanagasabapathi Sathasivan
School of Biological Sciences
The University of Texas at Austin

Kendall Hunt
publishing company

Cover photos courtesy of the author

White magnolia (*Magnolia macrophylla*) on the front cover and white peacock (*Pavo cristatus* mut. alba) on the back cover are from the botanical gardens of the Palazzo Borromeo, Isola Bella, Italy.

All interior art is courtesy of Goli Zarchi and Marianna P. Grenadier

www.kendallhunt.com
Send all inquiries to:
4050 Westmark Drive
Dubuque, IA 52004-1840

Copyright © 2006, 2012 by Kanagasabapathi Sathasivan

Revised Printing 2013

ISBN 978-1-4652-3444-5

Printed in the United States of America
10 9 8 7 6 5 4

CONTENTS

Preface

We live in an exciting time in history. Extensive research in the field of biology is helping us unravel the mysteries of life. With my profound interest in both teaching and research, the discoveries in biology never cease to amaze me. I value this opportunity to share my passion for biology with you, the reader. This book is a result of teaching introductory biology at the University of Texas at Austin for over two decades. Its contents are mainly from the summaries of my lecture notes, class handouts and study guide that were developed from reading several biology and biochemistry textbooks and from research papers in scientific journals. The objective of writing this book was to provide a concise and clear presentation of cell and molecular biology for undergraduate students to help them learn the concepts and apply them with critical thinking.

I am indebted to all my teachers, colleagues, teaching assistants and students for their encouragement, enthusiasm and constructive criticism, which helped me, improve my teaching and learning. In particular, I sincerely thank my Professors Norimoto Murai and Sue Bartlett from Louisiana State University who inspired me to teach. I am grateful to Professor Ahmad Islam, Kanaka Sathasivan, Mona Mehdy, Andrew Harper and Chris Martell for their critical review of this course guide. I acknowledge and thank Marianna Grenadier and Goli Zarchi for their skillful artwork and illustrations that help explain the concepts clearly. I greatly appreciate and thank Kendall-Hunt Publishing Company for the cover design, project management and timely publication in a professional manner. Above all, I am grateful to my wife, Kanthi and children, Kanaka and Sarathi, for their love, encouragement and support during the years I spent in preparing this book.

If you have any comments, suggestions or questions about this book, please e-mail me at DrSata@gmail.com.

Thanks and best wishes,
Dr. K. Sathasivan

BIG IDEA 1
STRUCTURE RELATES TO FUNCTION

Chapters

1. Introduction to Biology
2. Chemistry for Biology
3. Biological Molecules
4. Origin of Life
5. Cell Structure and Function
6. Cell Membrane
7. Cell Communication

1. INTRODUCTION TO BIOLOGY

Concepts

- Biological systems are structured at many levels that interrelate and interact.
- Cells and organisms are made of water and organic molecules with specific properties.
- Scientific methods validate predictions through experimentation by testing a hypothesis and finding substantial evidence.

Outline

I. Why Study Biology
II. Properties of Life
III. Scientific Approaches in Biology
IV. Classification System in Biology

1. Why study biology?

The study of biology helps us understand the nature of life and the mechanisms underlying life processes. In addition, we use biological knowledge for improving the environment or bettering quality of life, such as finding new cures for diseases and developing better plants and animals for agriculture.

Why is biology increasingly important today?

The last few centuries were dominated by major discoveries in chemistry and physics. The 21st century will see a major explosion of information from research being conducted in various disciplines of biological sciences merging with knowledge from other fields. More than half a million papers are published per year in biology alone. Consider that DNA, the secret code of life, was discovered only in 1953, but we have already sequenced the entire human genome. Applications are rapidly increasing in various fields including medical, agricultural and veterinary sciences.

Why study cellular and molecular biology?

The connecting basis of all life is at the cellular and molecular level. DNA, RNA, proteins and the cellular mechanisms behind each of these form the fundamental basis of life. Many biological phenomena are better understood at the biochemical and molecular level. This depth of study provides many opportunities: to genetically alter DNA or to develop cures and diagnostics to improve life in a fundamental and precise way. To study biology, we should start with the properties of living organisms by examining model systems and using broad approaches to studying life.

II. Properties of Life

Life as we know it is carbon-based, organic in nature and contains water. The basic unit of life is the cell. The emergent properties of living organisms are as follows:

- Reproduction: Life comes only from other life. The genetic material in all living cells is made of DNA.
- Growth and development: All living organisms go through growth and developmental stages.
- Order and structure: Living cells and organisms are highly ordered and structured. These structures correlate with their functions.
- Metabolism: Energy consumption and release happen constantly in a living organism. Organisms consume organic foods, minerals and other nutrients. They can make and breakdown large molecules through various metabolic processes.
- Respiration: Consuming oxygen and releasing carbon dioxide during the breakdown of food to generate energy is an essential process to sustain life.
- Response to environmental stimuli: Living organisms can sense environmental cues (their surroundings) and respond in an appropriate way. They can maintain internal conditions (homeostasis) in spite of changing surroundings.
- Adaptation and evolution: Living organisms adapt to their environment over short periods of their generation or over many generations. Over billions of years, life has adapted, changed and evolved to make new life forms.
- Autonomous movement: Living organisms such as bacteria, protists and animals can move autonomously. Fungi and plants normally grow towards sources of nutrition and/or light.

III. Scientific Approaches in Biology

Model systems

Since there are millions of living organisms, we cannot study every one of them in a detailed manner. Hence we use selected organisms known as model systems to study the mechanisms of life.

A model system is a representative organism or a cell type used for conducting simple or complex biological experiments. Model systems are normally easy to grow, manipulate and study. Studies already published on these model systems provide a vast amount of genetic information.

Some model systems are listed below:
- Prokaryotes: unicellular; cells have no nucleus
  - E. coli (*Escherichia coli*)
  - Salmonella (*Salmonella typhimurium*)
- Eukaryotes: uni- & multicellular organisms; cells have a membrane-bound nucleus and organelles
  - Plants: arabidopsis (*Arabidopsis thaliana*), corn (*Zea mays*) and rice (*Oryza sativa*)
  - Fungi: yeast (*Saccharomyces cerevisea*)
  - Animals: fruit fly (*Drosophila melanogaster*), nematode (*Caenorhab-*

ditis elegans), mouse (*Mus musculus*), zebra fish (*Danio rerio*) and human cell lines (*HeLa cells*)

Broad Approaches to Studying Life

Based on whether an entire organism or part(s) of an organism is used in an experiment, we can call the studies either holistic or reductionistic. **Holism** is an approach to studying whole organisms for behavioral, physiological and nutritional studies. For example, rats are used as a model system to study the effects of various drugs on aging. **Reductionism** is an approach to studying multicellular organisms at the cellular or tissue levels. Whole organisms are not used. Cells or tissues derived from the organisms are used to conduct experiments. For example, various cell lines of humans and cell suspensions of higher plants are used for cellular, biochemical and molecular studies.

Another way to describe a study is based on whether the experiment is done under living or non-living conditions. **In vivo studies** are experiments used to study physiology, ecology of organisms under living conditions. Examples: rats, rabbits, plant tissue culture, etc. These studies can be holistic or reductionist. **In vitro studies** are experiments performed under non-living (abiotic) conditions, e.g.in a test tube with known quantities of chemicals and enzymes added and incubated at a particular temperature, pH, etc. Such systems are used to study biochemistry, cell biology and molecular biology. These studies are strictly reductionistic in approach. **In situ studies** are experiments conducted to determine the presence of certain molecules such as DNA, RNA or protein in a particular site (say within a cell or tissue). For example, Fluorescent in situ hybridization (FISH) is used to determine which chromosome contains a particular gene. These are normally in vitro studies based on reductionism.

Scientific Reasoning

A scientific process usually starts with a hypothesis (a prediction that can be properly tested) followed by experimentation with proper controls, allowing conclusions to be drawn. The conclusions can be made using an inductive or deductive method. An **inductive method** uses specific conclusions and observations to make generalizations. For example, based on observing various species, Darwin was able to formulate a general concept of natural selection. A **deductive method** uses general concepts to deduce specific conclusions. For example, based on the fact that all birds have feathers, you can say that if the peacock is a bird, it should have feathers.

Hypotheses are formed based on observations or predictions. They must be testable and falsifiable by experimentation (e.g. gravity could be falsified if one were to observe objects being pushed from the Earth instead of pulled). Experiments must be conducted in controlled conditions (i.e. same temperature and pH) and with defined treatments. These include positive controls (have been tested and shown to work) and negative controls (should not work). For example, if you are conducting experiments on new antibiotics to kill *E. coli* then you will plate the bacteria in proper medium, each of them mixed with the different kinds of new antibiotics in separate plates. The positive control will have a known antibiotic and the negative control will lack an antibiotic.

Once the results of an experiment are repeated by several scientists under various conditions, they form a **theory**, a unifying concept. Examples include the theory of relativity and theory of evolution. If it is confirmed that an experiment's results are proven true at all times, the conclusions are formulated into a **law**. Examples include the laws of thermodynamics and Newton's laws of motion. Both theories and laws are considered scientific fact.

IV. Classification System in Biology

Taxonomic Classification

A standard classification system is important to group and classify the millions of living organisms. This system is periodically modified based on the consensus of several scientists at an international level. The current classification system can be summarized as follows.

Domain → Kingdom → Phylum → Class → Order → Family → Genus → Species

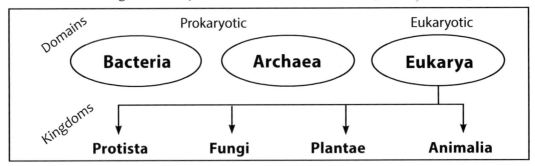

Figure 1-1. Taxonomic Classification

There are three domains into which all life is classified. **Bacteria** are a diverse group of unicellular prokaryotic organisms (no nucleus). **Archaea** is comprised of archaebacteria. These are prokaryotic but have some features of eukaryotic cells and can survive in extreme conditions. **Eukarya** includes both unicellular and multicellular eukaryotic organisms with a membrane-bound nucleus. Among eukaryotes, there are four kingdoms:
- Protista: unicellular, heterotrophic (e.g. paramecium, and amoeba)
- Fungi: multicellular and some unicellular, heterotrophic (e.g. yeast)
- Plantae: monocots and dicot plants, photosynthetic
- Animalia: multicellular, heterotrophic (all animals)

Biological Hierarchy

It is important to understand the complex biological systems are built from simple structures and at multiple levels of organization referred to as biological hierarchy. We study organisms and life at different levels of such organization in different experiments. The living world has a hierarchical order as explained below.
1. All organisms are made up of **atoms** (C, H, O, N, S and others) and **molecules** (water, amino acid, sugars).
2. Molecules combine to make **macromolecules** (proteins, carbohydrates, lipids, etc) which in turn make **parts of cells** (membrane, nucle-

us, mitochondria, etc.).

3. Parts of cells combine to form **cells** which can be unicellular organisms and the cells in multicellular organisms.

4. **Tissues** (bone, muscle, nerve, etc) of multicellular organisms are made of individual cells. Various tissues combine to make **organs** (heart, lungs, brain, etc.)

5. Several organs make up **organ systems** (circulatory, reproductive, etc). Multicellular **organisms** (plants, fungi and animals) contain many organ systems

6. **Population** is comprised of many organisms (many individuals of same species) and a **community** is a collection of populations in a limited area.

7. An **ecosystem** is a collection of communities. Several ecosystems may exist in a **biome** (desert, forest, tundra, etc.)

8. Biosphere is the living part of the earth in air, land and water. This includes all levels of biological hierarchy.

When you see a complex organisms such as a whale, elephant or a human being, it is good to understand the basic building blocks of such organisms and how they fit within the big picture of biological hierarchy.

2. CHEMISTRY FOR BIOLOGY

Concepts

- The number of protons defines the element; the number of neutrons defines the isotopes; and the number of electrons determines the chemical and physical properties of the atoms.
- Atoms combine to make molecules through covalent bonds, ionic bonds and hydrogen bonds.
- Molecules vary in their polarity due to the differences in electronegativity of the bonded atoms. Polarity may contribute to the above bonds and interactions.
- The polarity of water and hydrogen bonding between water molecules are responsible for many of the properties of water (e.g.: cohesiveness and high specific heat) that are essential to supporting life.
- Water is a major component of living organisms and participates in many essential biochemical reactions.
- The concentration of hydrogen ions, as measured by pH, affects the properties of biological molecules and influences biochemical reactions.
- Organic compounds, based on their structure and functional groups, vary in their size, shape and properties.

Outline

I.   Atoms and Molecules: basic definitions and concepts, chemical bonds and interactions
II. Water and Life: properties of water, aqueous solutions
III. Organic Molecules: carbon compounds, isomers and functional groups

All things living and non-living are made of simple atoms and molecules. In this chapter we will look at some basic terms and the different types of bonds and interactions between atoms and molecules.

1. Atoms and Molecules

Basic Definitions and Concepts

Matter is a substance that takes up space and has mass. An **element** is a substance made up only of a single type atom. It cannot be broken down to other substances by ordinary chemical or physical means. Elements are defined by the number of protons they have. An **atom** is the unit of matter. A **compound** consists of two or more different elements combined, while a **molecule** contains two or more atoms bonded together.

Atoms consist of 3 major particles: protons, neutrons, and electrons. Protons weigh 1 amu or Dalton and are positively charged. Neutrons also weigh 1 amu or Dalton and have no charge. Electrons weigh .001 amu or Dalton and are negatively charged. The sum of the number of protons and neutrons is referred to as the **mass number** (approximate mass). The **atomic weight** indicates to the absolute weight of an atom with reference to H or O and it is the average of isotopic weights of an element based on their abundance. The number of protons in each element is unique and is called the **atomic number**.

Living organisms contain about 25 elements. The 6 major elements that make up about 96 % of the living matter are C, O, H, N, S, and P. The elements Ca and K make up less than 3-4%. Other essential elements for life such as iron, magnesium and iodine are needed in small amounts and are called trace elements.

Isotopes of an element contain the same number of protons but varying number of neutrons. For instance, ^{12}C (6 protons and 6 neutrons) and ^{13}C (6 protons and 7 neutrons) are stable isotopes, whereas ^{14}C (6 protons and 8 neutrons) is a radioactive isotope. Stable isotopes can also be used for biological experiments when special methods are used to measure molecules based on their atomic weights. Radioisotopes emit radiation due to an unstable nucleus. Some radioisotopes are used in biological experiments to determine the age of a fossil or detect DNA and RNA. For example, ^{14}C has a half life ($t_{1/2}$; the time it takes for the element to lose half of its original mass) of 5,730 years. It is used for carbon dating and incorporation of carbon into various biological molecules. Stable isotopes emit no radiation. For example, ^{14}N and ^{15}N are used in labeling DNA and in mass spectroscopy.

Octet rule: An atom (the top few rows of periodic Table) needs 2 electrons in its first shell and 8 electrons in the second or third orbits to complete the valence shell. If the shell is complete, the atom is inert and stable. It does not need to bond with another atom to complete its valence shell. For example, helium, neon and argon are inert gases with 2 electrons in their first shell (He) and 8 each in their second (Ne) and third shells (Ar). If not, the atom is reactive and can interact and bond with other atoms to complete its valence shell. On the other hand, atoms such as oxygen needs tow more electrons to complete the valence shell, it makes bonds to share a pair of electrons with other atoms. There are also exceptions to octet rules.

Valence electrons are the electrons in the outermost orbit, which interact with other atoms. By analogy, if the nucleus is the size of a football, the electrons will be spinning a few miles away from it. The nuclei of two atoms do not come into contact with each other. Thus, all interactions in chemical bonds and chemical reactions are between electrons and sometimes protons. The only time a proton interacts with other atoms is in a simple hydrogen (H) atom, which is made of an electron and a proton. When H loses the electron, the proton (H^+) can interact with surrounding atoms.

The **valence** of an atom refers to its bonding capacity and is determined by how many unpaired valence electrons there are out of 8 (see Octet rule above). If there are 4 valence electrons (for example, carbon), the atom can make 4 covalent bonds, and its valence is 4. If there are 5 valence electrons, it can make 3 bonds, and its valence is 3; if 6, the valence is 2; and if 7, the valence is 1.

If atoms have 3 or fewer valence electrons, they tend to lose their electrons to their partners, as you can see in ionic bonding below, due to the stronger and more electronegative atom completely pulling the electrons to its valence shell. For example, the valence of H = 1, O = 2, N = 3, C = 4 and so on.

Electronegativity: The relative ability of an atom to attract electrons when it is combined with another atom. The stronger the electronegativity of an atom, the greater its affinity for the electrons from other atoms. The electronegativity depends on the number of valence electrons and the size of the atom. The top right corner in the Periodic Table consists of atoms with high electronegativity values. For example, fluorine has the highest value (4.0) followed by oxygen (3.5) compared to the lower values of carbon (2.5), sodium (0.9) and hydrogen (2.1). Electronegative atoms tend to form ionic bonds and also form cations (+) and anions (-). (See ionic bonding later in this chapter.)

Chemical Bonds and Interactions

Covalent bonding occurs when two atoms share a pair of electrons. This is the strongest of all bonds (~50-170 kcal/mol), present in all compounds and molecules. Specifically, the glycosidic bonds of carbohydrates, ester bonds of lipids, peptide bonds of proteins and phosphodiester bonds of DNA/RNA are all examples of covalent bonds. There are two kinds of covalent bonds. **Non-polar covalent bonding** occurs when two atoms, with the same or similar electronegativity, share electrons equally. **Polar covalent bonding** occurs when two atoms share electrons unequally, e.g. H_2O (see Figure 2.1) and NH_3. One of them (O or N) is more electronegative than the other (H).

Non-polar covalent bonds

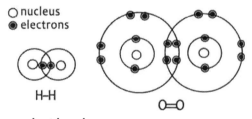

Figure 2-1. **Non-polar covalent bonds**

Ionic bonds form when the electronegativity of one atom is greater than that of the adjoining atom, the one with higher electronegativity pulls electrons to its valence shell from its neighboring atom, thereby becoming an anion (with a negative charge). The other atom becomes a cation (positive charge) after losing an electron. This generates ionic bonding due to the attraction of + and - charges (~3-7 kcal/mol). In a biological context, ionic bonds are weaker than covalent bonds, as they are found in low concentrations under aqueous surroundings. For example, in NaCl, Sodium (Na) has 11 electrons with 1 electron in its valence shell, and chlorine has a total of 17 electrons with 7 electrons in the valence shell. Chlorine gains the single valence electron from Na and becomes a chloride (Cl^-) ion (anion with negative charge), and sodium becomes a Na^+ ion (cation with positive charge). Ionic bonds can be found in proteins between positively- and negatively-charged amino acids.

H-bonding occurs when the hydrogen covalently attached to one electronegative atom is attracted to another electronegative atom. This attraction is called H-bonding; H- bonds (~3-7 kcal/mol) are similar to ionic bonds but stronger than van der Waals interactions or hydrophilic interactions. Examples include attraction between water molecules, H-bonds between H_2O and NH_3, and the H-bonds of DNA, RNA and proteins.

A **Van der Waals interaction** takes place when molecules interact there are pockets of constantly changing positive and negative charges. This takes place due to the changing distribution of electron clouds and results in weak forces of attraction. In addition, the spatial distribution of protons and neutrons in the nucleus of an atom affect their relative affinity for electrons. These temporary forces, though small (~1 kcal/mol), contribute to polarity of molecules and also van der Waals interactions within such molecules. Examples include lipids in biological membranes and cellulose in plant cell walls.

Hydrophilic and Hydrophobic interactions: Hydrophilic (water-loving) substances are normally polar, charged molecules that are soluble in water. Hydrophobic (water-fearing) molecules are normally non-polar, lipid-soluble molecules that are excluded from aqueous solutions by hydrogen bonding among polar molecules. Examples: The phospholipids in biological membranes have a hydrophilic region outside the membrane bilayer to interact with aqueous environment and a hydrophobic region inside the membrane bilayer. Amino acids with hydrophobic side chains tend to be in the interior portion of proteins while the amino acids with hydrophilic side chains can be either in the interior or exterior portion.

II. Water and Life

Water is essential for life as living organisms are made of up to 95 % water. In addition, water is the medium for and an important ingredient in many biochemical reactions. In this chapter, we will look at the properties of water and water-based (aqueous) solutions.

Water and H-bonding

In H-bonding, hydrogen and oxygen share electrons unequally, resulting in partial positive and negative charges on hydrogen and oxygen, respectively. The two electron orbitals of oxygen and two of hydrogen make the four corners of the water molecule which can make up to four H-bonds.

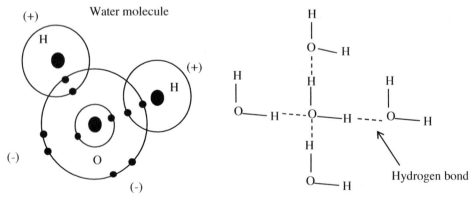

Figure 2-2. Water

Because of the two partial positive and two partial negative charges, water molecules can H-bond with up to four other water molecules. The relatively strong H-bonding in water is the main reason for its unique properties.

Properties of Water

1. **Cohesiveness:** Due to the constant forming and breaking of H-bonds in liquid water, H_2O molecules stick together: important for water uptake (transport from roots) and imbibition (water absorption by seeds).

2. **Adhesiveness:** Water can adhere to the surface of objects: important for the attachment of water (**adsorption**) that leads to absorption.

3. **High specific heat:** The specific heat of water (the heat energy required to increase temperature of water by 1 $^\circ C$) is 1 cal/g/$^\circ C$ compared to 0.1 cal/g/$^\circ C$ for iron and 0.6 cal/g/$^\circ C$ for ethanol. Water can absorb and release heat to stabilize the temperature in the surrounding area to make it habitable.

4. **High heat of vaporization:** It takes 540 cal to evaporate 1 g of water compared to 237 cal/g for ethanol and 59 cal/g for chloroform. This is important in evaporative cooling in animals and plants in hot weather.

5. **Freezing and expansion:** Water is densest at 4$^\circ C$ and expands during freezing at 0$^\circ C$ because the H-bonds between molecules in ice keep each molecule farther apart compared to liquid water. Due to lower density, ice floats on water keeping the water below warmer, providing a favorable environment for aquatic organisms to live under freezing cold conditions.

6. **Versatile solvent:** Water is an excellent solvent for all polar and charged molecules because of its polarity. Minerals and nutrients dissolved in water are available for easy uptake and transport by plants and animals.

7. **Medium for biochemical reactions:** Living cells contain up to 95% water, and many biochemical reactions in a cell occur under aqueous conditions.

8. **Ingredient of many biochemical reactions:** Many biochemical reactions need water as a reactant. For example, photosynthesis utilizes water to extract electrons to eventually fix carbon dioxide and synthesize sugars. Some reactions such as hydrolysis, uses water to break down complex molecules.

Aqueous Solutions

Water-based (aqueous) solutions have two major properties: solute concentration and H^+ ion concentration. A solute is a substance completely dissolved in a solvent.

Solute concentration: The solute concentration can be measured in molarity, weight or volume, and % of solid per unit volume. For example, a solution may have a concentration of 0.5 M sucrose, blood cholesterol may be measured as 200 mg/dL and you may buy milk with 2 % fat (2 g per 100 ml of milk). Molar concentrations are the most common units in scientific experiments.

Molecular weight (MW) is the sum of the weight of all the atoms in a molecule. Sometimes the formula weight (FW) is used to refer to the MW of a chemical formulation. MW is expressed in Daltons. For example, the MW of NaOH = 23 (Na) + 16 (O) + 1 (H) = 40 Da.

Mole (mol) is the MW expressed in grams for the practical purpose of dealing with two different solutes containing an equivalent number of molecules. It is based on Avogadro's number which defines one mole of any substance as 6.023×10^{23} molecules. For example, 1 mole of NaOH (40 g) contains the same number of molecules as 1 mole of sucrose (342 g) or 1 mole of any other substance. This concept helps us measure the accurate concentration of several atoms and molecules in a given solution.

Molarity (M) refers to the concentration of the number of moles of a solute dissolved in 1 liter of a solution. For example, knowing that the MW of NaOH is 40 Da, 1 M of NaOH means 40 g (1 mole) of NaOH are dissolved in 1 L of this solution. To make a 0.1 M solution, you need to have 4 g NaOH in a liter of solution. This is an important concept to understand for doing experiments in the biological laboratory. The fractions of molarity are expressed as follows:

1×10^{-3} M = 1mM (millmolar)
1×10^{-6} M = 1µM (micromolar)
1×10^{-9} M = 1nM (nanomolar)
1×10^{-12} M = 1pM (picomolar)
1×10^{-15} M = 1fM (femtomolar)

Making molar solutions

From solid to solution

Use the following formula

MW or FW (g/mol) x M (mol/L) x liters (L) = _____ g

If the units are not in molarity (M) or liters (L), then you need to convert the given unit to M and liters. For example, to make 100 mL of 0.5 M NaOH (MW = 40):

40 g/mol x 0.5 mol/L x 100 mL x 1 L/1000 mL = 2 g

One easy way to keep track of unit conversions is to write the equation like this:

40 g	0.5 mole	1 liter	100 mL	
1 mole	1 liter	1000 mL		=

The numbers across the top line are multiplied, the ones on the bottom are divided. Cross out the units that cancel.

40 g	0.5 mole	1 liter	100 mL	
1 mole	1 liter	1000 mL		= 2 g

From stock solution (solution 1) to a diluted solution (solution 2):
Use the following formula:

$$C_1V_1 = C_2V_2$$

Where C_1 is the concentration of stock solution 1.
C_2 is the concentration of working solution 2.
V_1 is the volume of stock solution you need to calculate.
V_2 is the volume of the working solution to be made.

You can use any units as long as the units are the same on both sides of the equation.
For example, to make 100 ml of 2 % NaCl from 10 % NaCl, you will set up the formula as 10 % V_1 = 2 % x 100 ml. Solve this to get v_1 as 20 ml of stock solution, and the remainder of volume (100 ml – 20 ml = 80 ml) will be water.

H^+ Concentration $[H^+]$: Acids, Bases and Buffers

In pure water, approximately one in 554 million molecules is ionized (dissociated) into H^+ and OH^- (hydroxide) ions. The concentration of H^+, written $[H^+]$, is equal to that of OH^-. At equilibrium, $[H^+] = [OH^-]$.

We can measure the $[H^+]$ in water or water-based solutions by using the concept of pH. The pH of a solution is a measure of the negative logarithm of its H^+ ion concentration in molar ($-\log_{10} [H^+]$). The negative log is used to simplify the molarity into positive numbers of pH. For an aqueous solution, pH varies from 1 to 14. For practical purposes, this is the range between minimum and maximum pH.

In any aqueous solution, the K_w (water constant) will be the product of $[H^+]$ and $[OH^-]$; $K_w = [H^+] \times [OH^-]$ and in pure water, it is 10^{-7} M x 10^{-7} M $= 10^{-14}$ M. The following table illustrates the changes in hydrogen and hydroxide ion concentrations in an aqueous solution.

pH	$[H^+]$	$[OH^-]$	K_w
5	10^{-5} M	10^{-9} M	10^{-14}
6	10^{-6} M	10^{-8} M	10^{-14}
7	10^{-7} M	10^{-7} M	10^{-14}
8	10^{-8} M	10^{-6} M	10^{-14}
9	10^{-9} M	10^{-5} M	10^{-14}

Remember that as the pH increases, the $[H^+]$ decreases and the $[OH^-]$ increases. Also note that when pH changes by one unit, the $[H^+]$ or $[OH^-]$ changes 10 fold because the pH units are logarithmic. For example, a solution with a pH of 4 has 100 times more $[H^+]$ than a solution with a pH of 6.

An **acid** is a chemical that increases the $[H^+]$. It can be considered a proton (H^+) donor because it increases $[H^+]$ in a solution, e.g.: HCl $\rightarrow$ H^+ + Cl^-. A **base** is a chemical that is either a proton acceptor or hydroxide donor that can decrease $[H^+]$ or increase $[OH^-]$ in a solution, e.g.: NH_3 + H^+ $\rightarrow$ NH_4 + NaOH $\rightarrow$ Na^+ + OH^- and then OH^- + H^+ $\rightarrow H_2O$. When a compound donates or accepts a proton, there must be another compound that accepts that proton or accepts an $[OH^-]$. These are called Conjugate acid (the result of a base accepting a proton), or conjugate base (the result of an acid donating a proton).

$$\text{Acid + Base} \quad \longleftrightarrow \quad \text{Conjugate Base + Conjugate Acid}$$

Aqueous solutions at pH 7 are called **neutral**, below pH 7 **acidic** and above pH 7 **basic**. Some examples are stomach acid, pH = 2 (acidic), blood, pH = 7.4 (slightly basic) and bleach, pH = 12.5 (basic).

A **buffer** is a substance that minimizes pH change by accepting excess H^+s when pH decreases or by donating H^+ when pH increases. Most buffers are weak acids or weak bases. For example, when pH increases carbonic acid (H_2CO_3) donates protons to become a base (HCO_3^-).

When pH increases

$$H_2CO_3 \text{ (Acid)} \rightarrow HCO_3^- \text{ (Conjugate Base)} + H^+$$

When pH decreases

$$(H^+\text{-donor/acid}) \leftarrow (H^+\text{-acceptor/base})$$

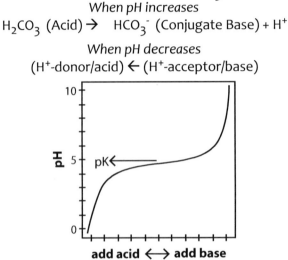

add acid $\longleftrightarrow$ add base

Figure 2-3. pH and pK

As you can see in the graph above, pK is the pH at which the ratio of the acid form of a compound to the base form is one, or equal. For example, in the above case, at a particular pH, the concentration of carbonic acid (H_2CO_3) is the same as that of bicarbonate (HCO_3^-). That pH (6.6) will be the pK for this buffer system. The buffer has the greatest capacity to maintain the pH of an aqueous solution around its pK value, e.g.: Trizma buffer has a pK value of 8.1 and is used for many DNA experiments where the optimum pH needed is from 7 to 9, the buffering range of Trizma. There are acidic, neutral or basic buffers with a pK in that respective range. Depending on the experimental system, one can choose an optimal buffer.

III Organic Molecules

Organic Molecules

Next to water, organic molecules (carbon-based) are the most abundant components in living systems. Carbon, hydrogen, nitrogen and oxygen, along with phosphorus and sulfur, are the major elements in living organisms and are present in similar percentages. All biological molecules are organic compounds of vast diversity. Simple organic compounds include hydrocarbons such as methane (CH_4) and ethane $(CH_3\text{-}CH_3)$ which contain few carbons. Complex organic molecules include large molecules (macromolecules such as proteins, polysaccharides, DNA and RNA) which may have millions of carbons connected together.

Organic compounds may be linear (aliphatic, e.g., glycerol), branched (isoleucine) or circular (aromatic, e.g., phenol and cholesterol), saturated (no double bonds between carbons, e.g., palmitic acid) or unsaturated (one or more double bonds between carbons, e.g., oleic acid). Organic molecules are represented by molecular formulas (e.g., CH_4) and structural formulas.

Chemical Structures

Sometimes, chemical structures are abbreviated. For example, cyclohexane (C_6H_{12}) can be represented by a hexagon:

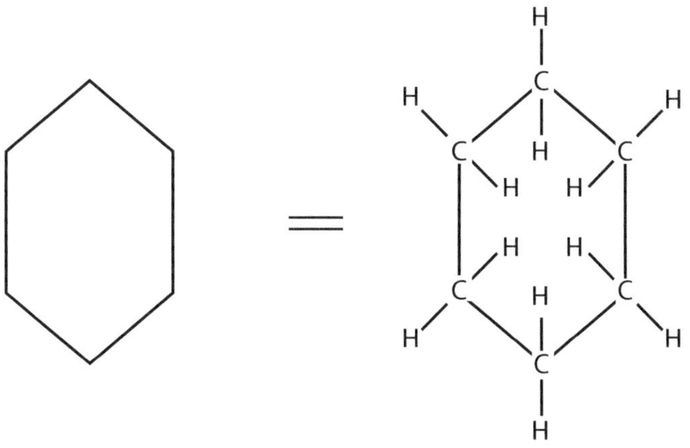

Or a $CH_3CH_2CH_2CH_2CH_3$ can be represented by a wiggly line.

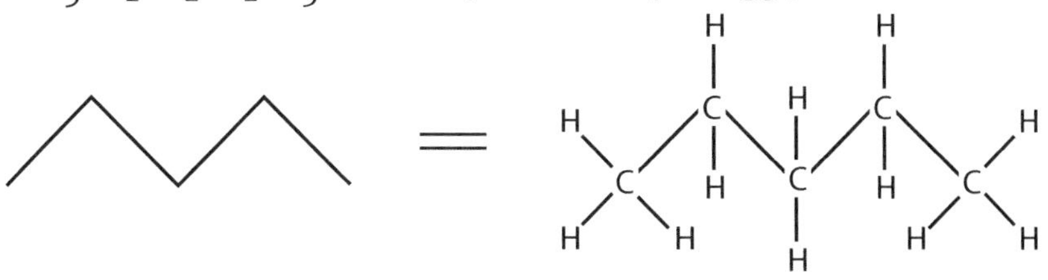

Whenever there is an oxygen or nitrogen in a carbon ring, it is written out but the carbons are not. For example, ribose is represented below:

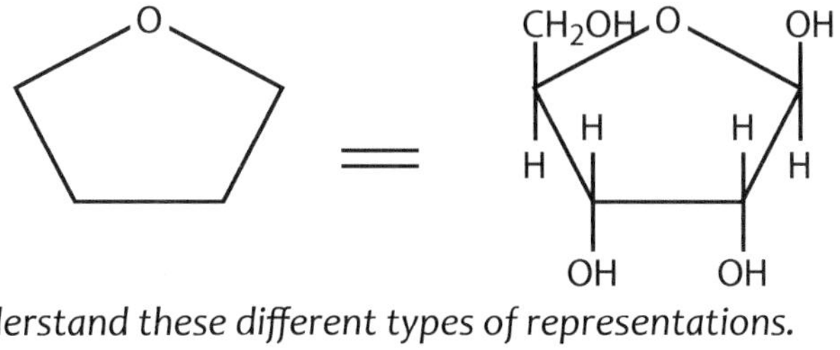

Learn to understand these different types of representations.

Isomers and Functional Groups

Isomers

Isomers are organic molecules with the same molecular formula but different structural formulas and different properties. They occur in three different types: structural, geometric and optical isomers.

1. **Structural isomers** have the same molecular formula but different structures, e.g.: leucine and isoleucine (side chains shown below). This

results in two different molecules, though they contain same number and type of atoms.

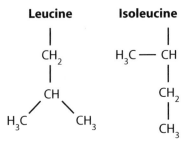

Figure 2-4. Structural isomers

2. **Geometric isomers** form due to the inflexibility of double bonds between the carbons. If the same types of functional groups are on the same side, the molecule is said to be in *cis* configuration, and if they are away from each other, it is called *trans* configuration.

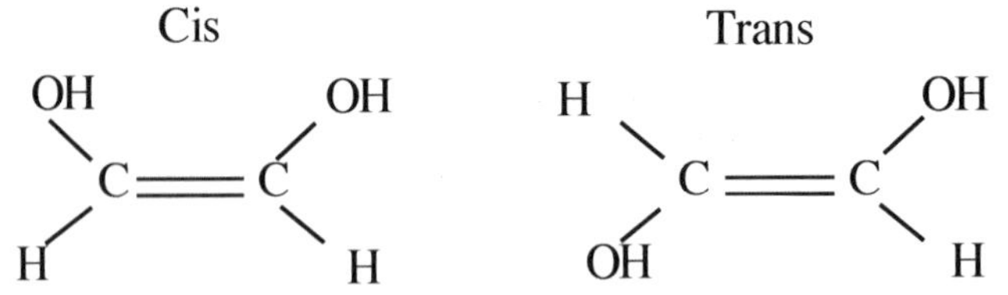

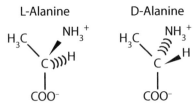

Figure 2-5. Geometric isomers

3. **Optical isomers or enantiomers** are mirror images of each other. Optical isomers occur when a carbon is attached asymmetrically to 4 different atoms or molecules, e.g.: L-amino acid (L = laevus/left-handed), used by cells, and D-amino acid (D = dexter/right-handed), rarely used and may be toxic to cells.

L-Alanine   D-Alanine

H_3C NH_3^+ H_3C NH_3^+
     C)))H   C   H
      | |
     COO⁻   COO⁻

Figure 2-6. Optical isomers

The 3- dimensional shape and nature of functional groups on each molecule determine the molecule's biological activity and usefulness. The functional groups are explained in next section.

Functional groups

Functional groups are atoms or groups of atoms, covalently bonded to the carbon skeleton. The functional groups greatly influence the property and reactivity of the organic molecule to which they are attached, based on their number and position.

1. **Hydroxyl group** (-OH): Since oxygen is electronegative and hydrogen is slightly positive, the -OH group confers polarity to the molecule. It makes the molecule easily soluble in water. Molecules with hydroxyl group(s) are generally called alcohols. Almost all carbohydrates, pro-

teins and nucleic acids contain -OH groups, e.g., sugars and alcohols.

2. **Carbonyl group** (-C=O): This is a slightly polar functional group. Organic solvents such as propanal and acetone contain -C=O groups. If it is at the end of an organic molecule, it is an aldehyde, e.g.: glucose. If it is in the middle, the molecule is a ketone, e.g.: fructose. Carbonyl groups are present in simple sugars, some proteins and nucleotides. A carbonyl group in simple sugars may react with an -OH group to form a ring structure.

3. **Carboxyl group** (-COOH): An acidic group that can ionize to form -COO- and H^+ to increase $[H^+]$ of the solution, e.g.: acetic acid, formic acid, citric acid and malic acid. The ionized forms of these molecules are acetate, formate, citrate and malate, respectively. The -COOH group is also present in all amino acids and proteins.

4. **Amino group** (-NH2): Amines can act as a base by accepting protons ($-NH_2 + H^+ = -NH_3^+$). An amino group is found in all amino acids, proteins and some specific nucleotides.

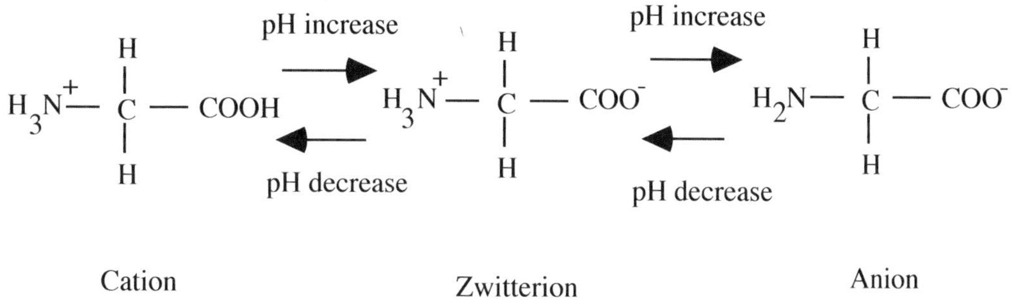

Figure 2-7. Cation (+), Zwitterion (+ and -), Anion (-)

5. **Sulfhydryl group** (-SH): A reactive group, -SH is present in the amino acid cysteine. Two such -SH groups within a protein can combine to make a disulfide bridge (-S-S-) to stabilize a protein structure. -SH groups are sometimes found in active sites involved in the catalysis of enzymes.

6. **Phosphate group** ($-OPO_3^{2-}$): Phosphate groups are highly polar and important in energy compounds such as adenosine triphosphate (ATP). They are also present in DNA, RNA and all nucleotides. Phosphate is found in phospholipids. P_i refers to inorganic phosphates and PP_i refers to pyrophosphate. This is an acidic and a reactive group.

7. **Methyl group** ($-CH_3$): As a non-polar functional group, methyl groups affect the solubility of a compound in aqueous or organic solutions. Methyl groups have a strong influence on the bioactivity of the molecule involved. Methylation (adding a methyl group) of a DNA molecule can make it non-functional. Methylation of some drugs or pesticides makes them more permeable through cell membranes. Methyl groups are found in alcohols, fatty acids, some amino acids and nucleotides.

3. BIOLOGICAL MOLECULES

Concepts

- Several subunit molecules are used to synthesize each class of biological molecules.
- Condensation/dehydration reactions help synthesize biological molecules in cells; hydrolysis reactions break down biological molecules.
- A simple monosaccharide like glucose can be used to construct many chemically distinct oligosaccharides and polysaccharides.
- Lipids are a class of biological molecules not classified as polymers. They are generally non-polar and form a wide variety of molecules.
- Phospholipids are amphipathic molecules that form the main structure of biological membranes.
- The structure of a fatty acid's hydrocarbon chain determines its properties as well as the properties and functions of the phospholipids and triglycerides made from it.
- Proteins are made of amino acids which interact with each other as the polypeptide folds.
- The overall 3-D shape of a protein is important for its optimal function and is formed by several bonds and interactions at multiple levels.
- When a globular protein folds in an aqueous solution, the hydrophilic R groups generally tend to be exposed on the surface of this protein while the hydrophobic R groups generally tend to be concealed inside.
- Denaturation causes a protein to unfold, making it nonfunctional.
- Nucleic acids (DNA and RNA) are polymers made of nucleotide monomers.
- The DNA double helix is formed by complementary base pairing and RNA forms variable secondary structures.

Outline

I. Condensation Synthesis and Hydrolysis
II. Carbohydrates
III. Lipids
IV. Proteins
V. Nucleic Acids

1. Condensation Synthesis and Hydrolysis

As covered in biological hierarchy in the first chapter, atoms combine to form molecules that are used to build macromolecules such as DNA, RNA, proteins, carbohydrates and lipids, all of which form the building blocks of life. The four major groups of biological molecules are **carbohydrates, lipids, proteins** and **nucleic acids**. Each part of the cell is composed of several different types of biological molecules. Some the biological molecules are small and are used as monomers to make larger molecules. Some are very large (1000s of Daltons) and are called macromolecules. The size limit for macromolecules is an arbitrary one. Simple sugars, amino acids, nucleotides and almost all lipids are relatively very small compared to macromolecules such as polysaccharides, polypeptides (proteins), DNA and RNA.

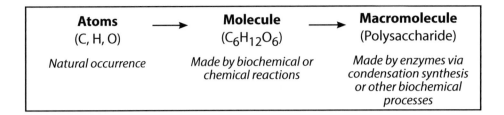

Atoms	→	**Molecule**	→	**Macromolecule**
(C, H, O)		($C_6H_{12}O_6$)		(Polysaccharide)
Natural occurrence		*Made by biochemical or chemical reactions*		*Made by enzymes via condensation synthesis or other biochemical processes*

The individual units that make up a larger molecule are called monomers. Monomers typically have attached –H and –OH groups. Two monomers are combined through a **condensation synthesis** to make a dimer by the removal of an -H and an -OH group, which form a water (H_2O) molecule. More monomers are added in a similar reaction to synthesize polymers.

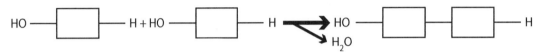

Figure 3-1. Condensation synthesis

Condensation synthesis of a macromolecule is performed by a specific enzyme that uses specific monomers to make that polymer. This reaction is also referred to as dehydrations synthesis and it creates bonds between the monomers in carbohydrates, lipids and proteins. Nucleic acids are polymerized by a similar reaction, including a nucleophilic attack.

Hydrolysis breaks down dimers, trimers or polymers into monomers by adding an -H and an -OH group derived from the splitting of a water molecule (hydro = water, lysis = break down). This is important for catabolic processes that utilize the energy stored in different macromolecules. Hydrolysis of a macromolecule is performed by a specific enzyme, almost always a protein catalyzing a reaction. Their names usually end with the suffix "ase" except when 'ase' is preceded by capital 'A,' the capital is removed, e.g.: cellulose is degraded by cellulase; DNA is degraded by DNase.

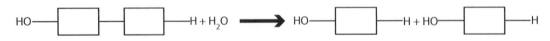

Figure 3-2. Hydrolysis

II. Carbohydrates

Monosaccharides

These simple sugars are the monomers (single units) that make up complex carbohydrates with many units. Simple sugars are made of C, H and O in a ratio of C:H2:O and are produced by photosynthetic organisms in the following reaction: CO2 + H2O +light ---------> CH2O + O2

The carbon skeleton size varies from 3 to 7 carbons, and an -OH group is attached to each C, except for one which is double bonded to an O (carbonyl-CO). If -CO is at the end, it is an aldose sugar, e.g., glucose, if -CO is in the middle, it is a ketose sugar, e.g., fructose.

In aqueous solutions, sugars with 5-7 carbons form a ring structure. A hexose such as glucose forms a ring structure with the -C=O group in the 5th C, bonding with the -OH group in the first C. When such ring structures form, if the -OH group on first C is below the plane of the ring, it is a α-glucose and if it is above the plane, it is a β-glucose.

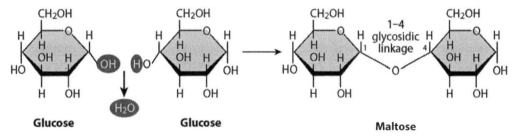

Linear and ring forms of glucose

Figure 3-3. Linear and ring forms of glucose

Functions:
1. Provides a major source of energy for cells, e.g.: glucose and fructose
2. Energy stored in sugars is harvested by cells through respiration
3. Carbon skeletons are used for making other molecules

Disaccharides

These are formed by enzymes which combine two monosaccharides through **glycosidic linkages**.

glucose + glucose	→	maltose
glucose + galactose	→	lactose
glucose + fructose	→	sucrose

Glucose   **Glucose**   **Maltose**

Figure 3-4. Maltose, dehydration reaction

Alpha and beta linkages

The two different glycosidic linkages are named based on the position of the -OH group attached to the first C of the monosaccharide. As we saw earlier, if the -OH group is below the plane of sugars, it is an α-linkage, and if it is above the plane, it is a β-linkage. This positioning occurs during the cyclization (ring formation) of monosaccharides by the specific enzyme involved in disaccharide biosynthesis. These linkages determine the properties of the resulting carbohydrates. Numbers in α-1, 4 or β-1, 4 indicate the linkages between the first C of monosaccharide-1 and the 4th C of monosaccharide-2. The type of linkage defines the properties of the carbohydrates and is critical in deciding whether the polymer will be broken down into monomers.

Polysaccharides

Polysaccharides are long chains of carbohydrates with several thousands of monomers. Shorter chains of carbohydrates are called **oligosaccharides** (~ 5 to 20 sugar molecules). Polysaccharides can be grouped into storage and structural forms based on their structure and function.

Storage polysaccharides are used for energy utilization. Examples:
1. _Starch_: α-1,4 linked glucose, amylose and amylopectin in plants; major storage products in potato, rice, wheat and corn.
2. _Glycogen_: similar to starch but highly branched, α-1, 4 linked polysaccharide stored in the liver and muscles of animals.

Both starch and glycogen are easily digestible by humans.

Structural polysaccharides are used to build cell walls and exoskeletons. Examples:
1. _Cellulose_: β-1,4 linked glucose molecules; major constituents of plant cell walls, the most abundant biopolymers on earth. Cellulose can be degraded by cellulase enzyme made by wood-rotting fungi and bacteria.
2. _Callose_: shorter than cellulose, contains β-1, 3 linked glucose molecules, formed at wounding sites in plants.
3. _Chitin_: b-1, 4 linked N-acetyl glucosamine; major structural component of exoskeletons of insects and cell walls of fungi. Chitin in fungal cell walls can be degraded by chitinase enzyme made by plants as a part of defense mechanisms against fungi.

III. Lipids

Lipids are highly non-polar and hydrophobic. They are soluble in organic solvents such as ether and chloroform. They have several functions including storage of energy (9 cal/g of fat), insulation against heat loss, cushioning vital organs and as part of the lipid bilayer in biological membranes. Lipids can also serve as vitamins, pigments, growth hormones or regulators. There are three major kinds of lipids: fats (triglycerides), phospholipids and other lipids such as cholesterol, steroid hormones and carotenoids etc.

Triglycerides or fats

Glycerol (a 3-carbon alcohol) combined with fatty acids (a long hydrocarbon chain with a -COOH group) makes up fat, which may be mono-, di-, or triglyceride, depending on the number of fatty acids it contains. For example, glycerol and three fatty acids forms triglyceride. The covalent bond formed between an alcohol (glycerol) and an acid (fatty acid) is called **ester bond**. Depending upon whether one or two fatty acids are combined with a glycerol, they are called mono- or diglyceride respectively.

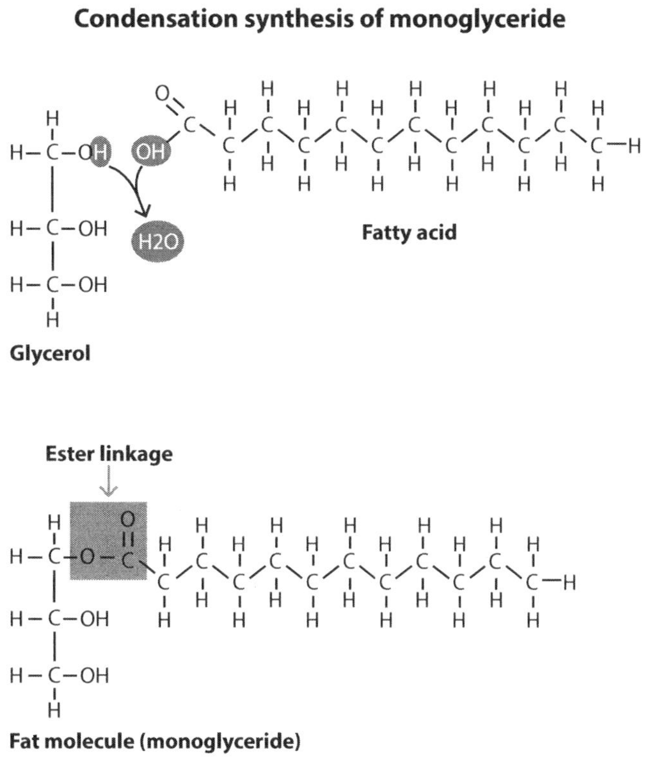

Condensation synthesis of monoglyceride

Figure 3-5. Ester linkage in monoglyceride/monoacylglycerol

The fatty acids in fats may be saturated (with hydrogen in all carbons) or unsaturated (with double bonds in the hydrocarbon chain). If there is a single double bond, it is mono unsaturated, and if there are 2 or more double bonds, it is called polyunsaturated. The differences between saturated and unsaturated fats are listed below.

Saturated Fats	**Unsaturated Fats**
Fatty acid carbon chain saturated with H	Not saturated with H
No double bonds or kinks between Cs	One or more double bonds
Usually solid at room temperature	Liquid at room temperature
Closely packed to each other	Not packed close together
Animal fats, tropical oils, coconut oil	Plant fats, temperate oils, coconut oil, canola oil

The greater the saturation level of the hydrocarbon, the higher is the T_m (melting temperature) of the fat.

Phospholipids

Glycerol + 2 fatty acids + a phosphate group + another chemical group (serine, choline etc.) make up phospholipids. Phospholipids have both hydrophilic and hydrophobic properties (amphipathic) due to the presence of the phosphate group and fatty acids, respectively. They are major components of lipid bilayers which separate different parts of cells and maintain the compartments of membrane-bound structures.

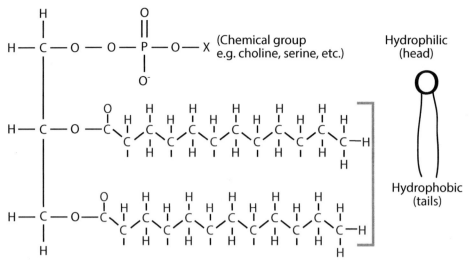

Figure 3-6. Phospholipid

Other lipids

Carotenoids: color pigments used for photosynthesis in plants and for vitamin-A synthesis in animals. These are made from 5-C isoprene units, e.g., b-carotene.

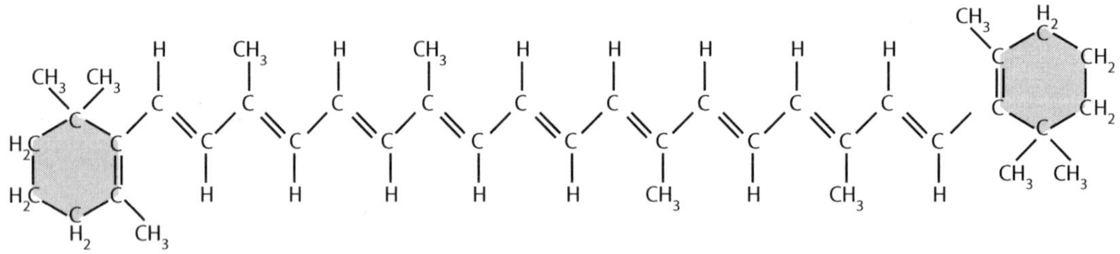

Figure 3-7. Carotenoid

Steroids: lipids with 4 fused C-rings, e.g., cholesterol, growth hormones such as testosterone, estrodiol.

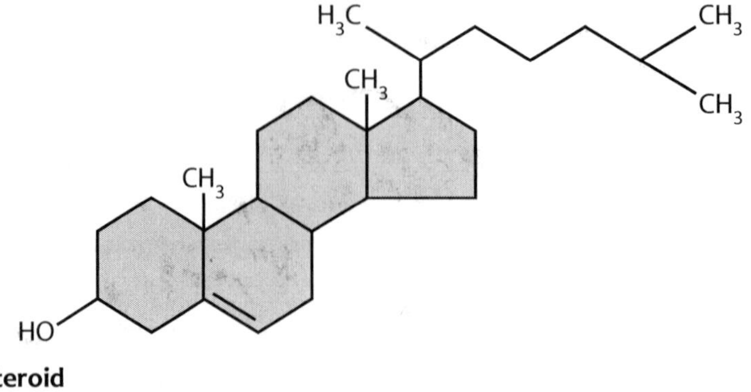

Figure 3-8. Steroid

IV. PROTEINS

Features

Proteins are made up of 20 different amino acids and are the most structurally diverse molecules, designed to suit different functions. They constitute about 50% of the dry weight of living cells. Proteins have several different functions: (a) structural (keratin, collagen), (b) storage (casein, ovalbumin), (c) transport (ion channels, hemoglobin), (d) metabolism (enzymes), (e) hormones (insulin), (f) defense (antibodies), (g) contractile (actin, myosin), (h) signaling (receptors), and (i) movement (microtubules, microfilaments).

Amino acids are the building blocks of all proteins. All amino acids contain an amino group and a carboxylic group and they can be grouped into various classes based on the nature of their side chains.

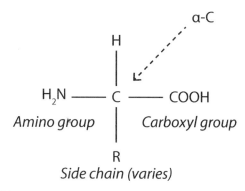

Figure 3-9. Amino acid

Side Chain Characteristics	Examples
Non-polar (hydrophobic)	glycine, alanine, valine, leucine, and isoleucine, phenylalanine, tryptophan, methionine, proline
Polar (hydrophilic)	serine, threonine, asparagine, glutamine
Acidic (-ly charged)	aspartic acid, glutamic acid
Basic (+ly charged)	arginine, histidine, lysine
Linear or unbranched	methionine, cysteine
Branched chain	leucine, isoleucine, valine
Aromatic	phenylalanine, tryptophan, tyrosine
-S-containing	methionine
-SH containing	cysteine
-OH containing	serine, threonine, tyrosine
Imino acid	proline

 Be able to recognize the different groups of amino acids from the given structure. No need to memorize specific amino acid names and structures.

Peptide bond

The bond formed between two amino acids during protein synthesis by ribosomes is called a **peptide bond** and a protein containing many amino acids is called **polypeptide**.

A peptide bond is formed by condensation synthesis by removing a H_2O molecule similar to the formation of ester bonds in lipids or glycosidic bonds in sugars. Peptide bonds are relatively rigid due to the C=O double bond which resonates its strength to the C-N bond making it less flexible.

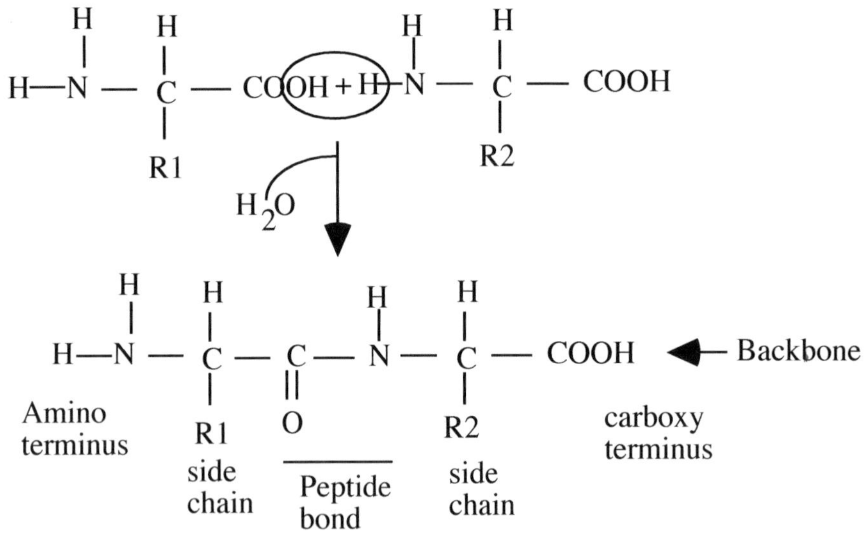

Figure 3-10.Peptide bond in protein synthesis; condensation synthesis

Protein Structure

The three-dimensional structure of proteins is complex, elegant, and is critical for its function. It can be described at four different levels.

1. **Primary structure**: amino acid sequence of a protein; determined by genes, the coding sequence of DNA. Since there are 20 amino acids, the possibilities of different combinations of proteins are numerous, i.e. 20^n with n = number of amino acids in a protein. The primary structure is stabilized by peptide bonds. The amino acid sequence determines the higher levels of a protein's structural organization. A different sequence of amino acids will result in a different protein with possibly, a different function. Small changes in a primary structure (due to mutations in DNA) may result in a defective protein.

2. **Secondary structure**: regular, repeated patterns of folding of the polypeptide, stabilized by H-bonding between the -C=O group of one amino acid and the -NH group of another along the polypeptide backbone. Two major types:
    Alpha-helix: is one type of secondary structure wherein the -NH group of residue *n* is H-bonded to the -C=O group of residue *n*-4. Alpha-helices are found in fibrous proteins such as keratins (found in skin, claws, nails, hair and wool) and also both inside and outside of the globular proteins.

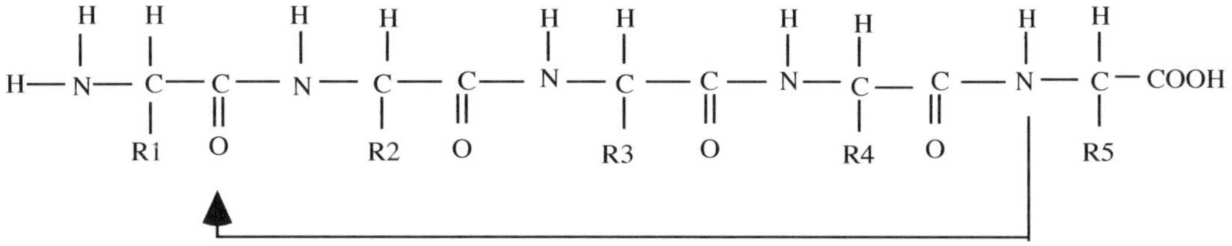

Figure 3-11. Alpha-helix

β-*pleated sheet*: This secondary structure is formed when H-bonding occurs between the -NH group of one strand of a protein with the -CO group of another strand of the same or different protein. The two strands may be running parallel to each other or antiparallel, e.g., silk fibers.

There are other secondary structures such as coils and loops that are less defined than the ones mentioned above.

3. **Tertiary structure**: It offers major contribution to the overall 3-D structure of a protein. Tertiary structure is formed due to irregular bonding between the side chains of various amino acids within a protein. **Hydrogen bonding** may happen between two R-groups such as alanine and aspartate ($-CH_2OH$ <---> $^-OOC-CH_2-$). Two non-polar amino acids with methyl groups in their side chains such as alanine-alanine ($-CH_3$: $_3HC-$) may form **hydrophobic interactions**. The attraction between an negatively charged acidic and positively charged basic amino acid such as aspartate and lysine ($-COO^-$ <---> $3HN^+-$) will result in **ionic bonding**. When two sulfhydryl groups (-SH+HS-) combine, it will form a covalent **disulfide bond** (-SS-) after releasing H_2.

4. **Quaternary structure**: interaction of two or more polypeptides or subunits of multimeric proteins (i.e.: containing several smaller subunits). The bonding can be a combination of ionic bonding, H-bonding, hydrophobic interaction and disulfide bridges, e.g., a and b subunits of hemoglobin. **Triple helix** Three separate strands of proteins are wound on each other and H-bonded to each other, e.g., collagen in cartilage. Collagens are rich in glycine, proline and hydroxy-proline. Cartilages are found under skin and in the tail of a rat.

How to determine protein structure

The 3-D structures of proteins are very important in understanding their function and interaction with other components of cells or chemicals. Scientists determine protein structures through various methods including (a) X-ray crystallography using crystal structures of proteins; (b) protein denaturation and renaturation studies by changing pH; and (c) prediction based on known sequence and structural information.

V. NUCLEIC ACIDS

There are two kinds of nucleic acids, ribonucleic acid (RNA) and deoxyribonucleic acid (DNA). RNA is made of monomers called nucleotides containing a nitrogenous base + a ribose + a phosphate group. DNA is made of monomers called deoxynucleotides containing a nitrogenous base + a deoxyribose + a phosphate group.

Functions

1. Nucleotide ATP (adenosine triphosphate) is the major form of cellular energy. ATP is made of a ribose + an adenine + 3 inorganic phosphates.
2. Nucleotides can accept and transport electrons, e.g.: NAD^+ (Nicotinamide Adenine Dinucleotide).
3. Some nucleotides serve as signal molecules, e.g.: cAMP (cyclic adenosine monophosphate).
4. Hereditary; DNA molecules store genetic information, and they are replicated and passed on from generation to generation.

Nucleotides and Nucleosides

Two kinds of nitrogenous bases:

Purines:	Adenine (A), Guanine (G)
Pyrimidines:	Cytosine (C) and Thymine (T) in DNA
	Uracil (U)- in RNA instead of T

Nucleoside: nitrogenous base + ribose sugar
Nucleotide: nitrogenous base + ribose sugar + phosphate

If the nucleotide has one phosphate, it is called nucleoside monophosphate (NMP); two phosphates, nucleoside diphosphate (NDP); three phosphates, nucleoside triphosphate (NTP). If the sugar is deoxy ribose as in DNA, then its monomer is called deoxyribonucleoside triphosphate (dNTP). If there are no oxygens in both the 2' and 3' carbons, then it is referred to as dideoxynucleoside triphosphate (ddNTP).

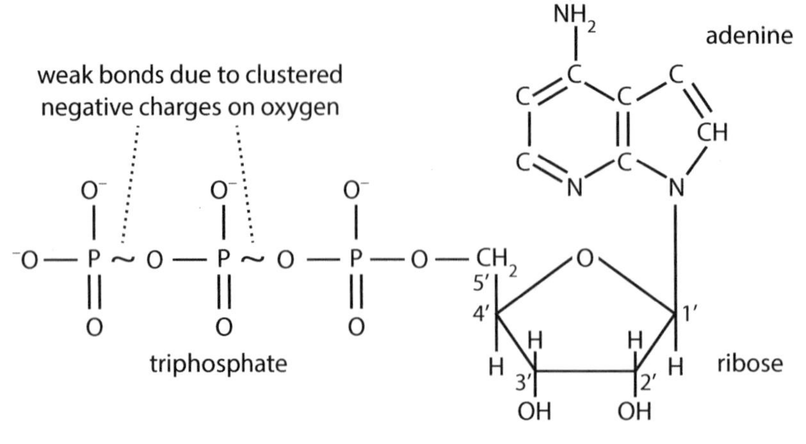

Figure 3-12. Nucleotide

DNA: Mostly present as a double-stranded double helix. Base pairing between the two strands is complementary; guanine pairs with cytosine (G:C) and adenine pairs with thymine (A:T) through H-bonding. It stores genetic information in its sequence and codes for RNA. DNA is more stable than RNA because it is double stranded and it lacks 2'-OH group. The 5' carbon of one nucleotide is linked to the 3' carbon of the next through phosphodiester linkages; this results in DNA strands having an unlinked 5' end and an unlinked 3' end. During DNA transcription and replication, DNA or RNA is made from the 5' end to the 3' end.

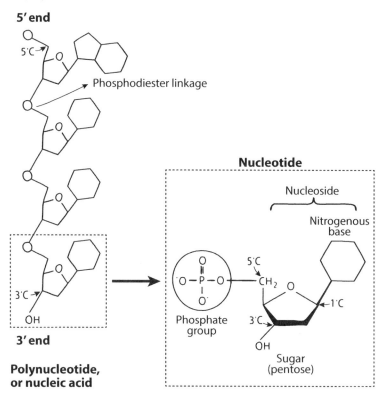

Figure 3-13. Nucleic acid and nucleotide

RNA: Mostly present as single-stranded with a complex and variable secondary structure. Base pairing, through H-bonds, is complementary; adenine pairs with Uracil (A:U) instead of thymine, and guanine pairs with cytosine (G:C). There are three major kinds of RNA:

mRNA (messenger RNA): carries information from DNA to be translated into protein

rRNA (ribosomal RNA): major part of ribosomes involved in protein synthesis

tRNA (transfer RNA): involved in transferring amino acids during protein synthesis

4. ORIGIN OF LIFE

Concepts

- Inorganic molecules possibly combined to form the building blocks of life which led to ancestral forms of life.
- Conditions during the early stages of Earth's history were conducive to such formation of life.
- RNA may possibly be the first genetic material as it can store information and catalyze reactions.

Outline

I. Hypotheses about the Origin of Life
II. Early Fossils and History of Life
III. Possible Sources of Origin
IV. The RNA World
V. Classification of Current Life Forms

1. Hypotheses about the Origin of Life

Before we make a transition from macromolecules to living cells, we should try to understand how life started in the first place, the history of life on earth and then how simple forms of life originated. Once we make an educated hypothesis about the origin of simple life forms then we can test this possibility based on (a) historical evidence or (b) simple experiments conducted under simulated conditions.

In the first chapter, we looked at the emergent properties of life, scientific approaches to studying life and the development of alternate hypotheses that can be tested. It is important to understand that many ideas, particularly spiritual or religious traditions, about the origins of life cannot be tested scientifically. Remember that scientific hypotheses must be falsifiable. However, the idea that a supernatural being created life cannot be falsified, meaning one could never perform an experiment or make an observation that contradicted this idea. This does not mean the idea is automatically true, only that cannot be a scientific hypothesis.

There are two major scientific hypotheses that can be tested to learn about the origins of life on earth: panspermia and abiogensis. Panspermia explores whether life came from another planet (extraterrestrial) or not, based on the proposal that meteors from space came with either simple living organisms or the complex molecules needed to start life on earth. Even if this is true, then we need to think about how life originated in the planet of such primary source. This leads to the second hypothesis that life originated "spontaneously" on earth or any other planet from simple atoms and molecules combining under high temperature in the presence of water, lightning, limited availability of oxygen, and other conditions of early earth. Let us look into the details of this second and the main hypothesis currently accepted by scientists.

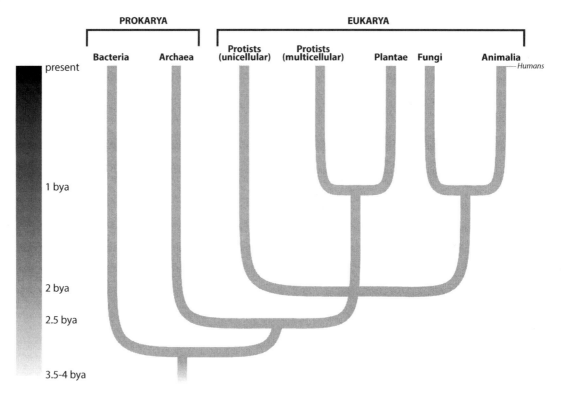

Figure 4-1. Tree of life with evolutionary timeline (bya = billions of years ago)

11. Early Fossils and History of Life

This approach of looking at the past to understand current conditions is similar to the detective work involved in understanding how an incident happened. The detective looks at the evidence left at the site, analyzes the samples he collects and gathers information about the time frame in which the events may have unfolded. The evidence scientists collect to study the origin of life are the fossils deposited during geological ages at different places on the earth. Such specimens are systematically analyzed with the help of certain radioisotopes that decay over a long period of time. Based on the current level of such radioisotopes in those specimens compared to the current isotopic distribution in nature, one can conclude the approximate age of the specimen. Using this approach, information has been collected about the geological time scale during which some of these bacterial and eukaryotic fossils lived. In addition, using both fossil evidence and DNA sequence comparisons, we can establish that life evolved from simple to complex forms.

The age of the Earth is about 4.5 billion years. Life started about 500 million years after the Earth's formation. Simple bacteria evolved about 4 billion years ago (bya) and lived on chemicals (chemotrophic). Photosynthetic cyanobacteria (autotrophic), originated around 2.5 bya. They were able to fix carbon dioxide into simple sugars and released oxygen into the atmosphere. This made the atmosphere rich in oxygen and allowed the formation and survival of aerobic organisms including eukaryotes. Around 1.8 bya, the oldest unicellular eukaryotic organisms started to appear and about 1.7 bya, multicellular organisms appeared. The last 500 million years saw an explosion of various life forms in both plants and animals. The lineage that led to modern humans broke off around 6 million years ago, and our species, *Homo sapiens,* evolved within the last 200,000 years. Now that we understand the history of life on Earth, the next question is how the first simple life forms came into existence.

III. Possible Sources of Origin

We have learned in previous chapters that atoms combine to make molecules. These then combine to make macromolecules that constitute parts of cells, which can eventually form cells. The transition from non-living chemicals to living cells may have taken millions or even billions of years and was not an overnight process.

In the 1920s, Russian scientist Oparin and British scientist Haldane independently proposed that the reducing conditions in early Earth's atmosphere or near volcanic regions under the ocean may have helped to form complex molecules from simple molecules. Reducing conditions favor the adding of electrons. The energy to form complex molecules may have been provided by high temperatures and UV radiation. It is virtually impossible to recreate the atmospheric conditions of early earth but scientists can simulate some aspects. To show that life could have formed from simple chemicals available 4 bya, Miller and Urey conducted an experiment in 1953 with some basic molecules. They used hydrogen, water, methane and ammonia in a setup with high power electrodes in order to simulate lightning to provide energy for further reactions. After cooling the reaction products, they noticed that simple organic molecules including urea, organic acids, simple sugars, amino acids had been formed. This showed that monomers of complex molecules could have formed under the reducing atmosphere present in the early periods of the Earth's history.

The next question is where these reactions may have taken place. Since water is an essential component of living cells, a good possibility is shallow water beds exposed to the reducing atmosphere or deep ocean vents that are rich in methane and sulfur. In addition to water and a reducing environment, the polymerization of monomers may need a substratum or a solid base for attachment. Rock, clay or pyrite (Fool's gold made of iron and sulfur) may have been the base for these reactions to occur.

Once simple monomers and macromolecules are formed, they can aggregate to form simple structures called **protobionts**. Oparin proposed that these bubble-like structures were essential for cells to evolve and to keep internal conditions separate from the surrounding environment. These protobionts can incorporate other macromolecules such as nucleic acids and proteins. Simple liposomes (lipid bodies) have been shown to be formed by the aggregation of lipids in an aqueous situation and would be able to provide structural support allowing complexity to evolve.

ATOMS → MOLECULES → MONOMERS → MACROMOLECULES → PROTOBIONTS
(natural)   (reducing conditions)   (polymerization on solid support)   (self-assembly)

This type of accumulation of macromolecules may have happened several times over millions of years before the right combination survived and replicated. However, such a combination was far from being able to replicate with precision equipped with proper genetic information. The next question is how life moved from organic molecules to the first self-replicating cells.

IV. The RNA World

For life to originate and perpetuate, you need to have a molecule that can be used to store information and also to catalyze the synthesis of other molecules. Thomas Cech of the University of Colorado, Boulder, recognized that RNA had this capability and compiled several pieces of chemical evidence that RNA molecules could catalyze simple reactions. In addition to its catalytic activity (RNA with catalytic activity is called a **ribozyme**), RNA can form a variety of secondary structures similar to proteins, which may have allowed the formation of a self-replicating cell. Recently, scientists have shown that RNA can form spontaneously in prebiotic conditions similar to those in the Miller-Urey experiment. Furthermore, the existence of ribosomal RNA and transfer RNA which participate in protein synthesis in modern cells lends more credence to this hypothesis.

This evidence supports the idea that RNA was probably the first genetic molecule to store information and to catalyze self-replication or even protein synthesis to start life. Once proteins (enzymes) are made, they can make carbohydrates and lipids. It is proposed that DNA evolved later to be a more stable molecule than RNA and proteins evolved to be more efficient enzymes. There are other plausible hypotheses about the origin of life, such as a "metabolism-first" model, but they need additional support and evidence.

V. Classification of Current Life Forms

The evolution of complex multicellular organisms from simple unicellular organisms and the evolution of complex internal structures at both cellular and organism level must have been gradual and taken several hundreds of millions of years in between different stages. In order to capture the history and evolutionary relationship of these organisms, scientists classify life into several categories, starting with domains and kingdoms.

For the first few billion years of its history, the Earth was occupied by prokaryotic and unicellular eukaryotic organisms. Only in the last billion years or so, multicellular organisms evolved. In the initial classification system, the organisms were grouped into bacteria, fungi, protists, plants and animals. Scientists now classify organisms into three domains, under which Eukarya is divided into four kingdoms: Protista, Fungi, Plantae and Animalia. Scientists are currently considering dividing protists into separate sub-kingdoms as they are well-defined groups within the kingdom Protista.

5. CELL STRUCTURE AND FUNCTION

Concepts

- Both the unity and diversity of cells reflect evolutionary history.
- Information is stored in genes and is expressed in gene products that are used to build cells.
- Cell structure is dynamic and requires external sources of energy.
- There are pathways associated with synthesis and delivery of gene products to, within and outside of the cell.
- The movement of cells (or organelles within cells) depends on motor proteins and the cytoskeleton.

Outline

I. Study of the cell
II. Overview of cells
III. The Nucleus
IV. Ribosomes
V. Endomembrane system
   (smooth ER, rough ER, Golgi, lysosomes, microbodies)
VI. Energy organelles
   (chloroplasts, mitochondria)
VII. Cytoskeleton
   (microtubules, microfilaments, intermediate filaments)
VIII. Cell surface
   (cell wall, cell junctions)

Cells are the basic units of life. As we have seen in the first chapter, there are two major kinds of cells, namely, prokaryotic (without nucleus) and eukaryotic (with nucleus). In this chapter, we will cover the methodology to study cells in general and the details of the structure and functions of all the components of the prokaryotic and eukaryotic cells.

I. Study of the Cell

Cell structure is observed mainly by microscopy using light and electron microscopes. Cell function is studied mainly by biochemical and molecular approaches supported by microscopy.

1. Microscopy

There are 2 important factors in microscopy, namely, magnification (how big) and resolution (how clear). **Magnification** of a light microscope is up to ~ 1500x and magnification of an electron microscope can be up to ~ 250, 000x. The units of linear measurement and examples of what you can observe in such units are as follows:

1m	=	100 cm or 1000 mm	1m	human body
1 mm	=	1/1000th of a m	1×10^{-3} m	human hair
1 µm	=	1/1000th of a mm	1×10^{-6} m	mitochondria
1 nm	=	1/1000th of a µm	1×10^{-9} m	molecule
1 A (Å)	=	1/10th of a nm	1×10^{-10} m	atom

(Å = Angstrom)

The **resolution** or resolving power of a microscope sets the practical limits of magnification for any microscope. The resolving power is inversely proportional to wavelengths of light. The light microscope is limited in its magnification power of 1500x and resolution of 0.2 µm. The electron microscope can resolve up to 0.2 nm. The structures viewed under the electron microscope are called ultrastructures.

Light microscope
Light is focused on the specimen through a condenser lens, and light passing through the specimen is refracted through the objective lens and ocular lens to magnify the subject. You can use the light microscope to observe live specimens in their natural colors or with stains.

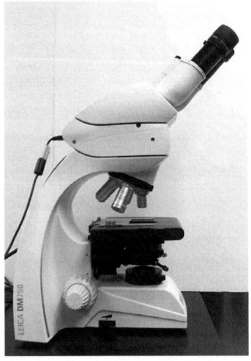

Figure 5-1. Light microscope

Transmission electron microscope (TEM)
Electron beams are aimed at a thin section of a specimen stained with metal to absorb electrons and enhance the contrast. Electrons transmitted through the specimen are focused and the image is magnified by electromagnetic lenses. TEM is used to study internal ultrastructures and cross-sections of cells or structures.

Scanning electron microscope (SEM)

Electron beams scan the surface of a specimen coated with gold. Scanning beams excite the secondary electrons on the sample surface, which are then collected and focused by the electromagnetic lens. Used to view the surface features and the 3-D shape of ultrastructures. The magnified images in both TEM and SEM are viewed on a screen and can be captured by cameras.

2. Cell fractionation

In cell fractionation, centrifugation is used to disrupt cells; various speeds and durations of centrifugation are used to isolate cellular components based on their density, size and shape. Fractionation involves a few basic steps.

1. Harvest tissues that are fresh or use stored tissue kept frozen at -70C or in liquid N_2. This is important to preserve the contents such as organelles, DNA, RNA or proteins which might otherwise be degraded.
2. Grind cells with liquid N_2 or in a suitable buffer. The liquid N_2 keeps enzymes, which may degrade cell contents, inactive.
3. Homogenize the cells in a suitable buffer. The solution contains salt, a buffer and some preservatives.
4. Centrifuge at various speeds and for various durations to isolate the components.

Centrifuges

Centrifuges are used to separate solutes in solution by using centripetal acceleration. By spinning rapidly, centrifuges place a force on the solutes, causing denser substances to move to the bottom of the tube, leaving lighter substances (and the solute) at the top of the tube.

Figure 5-2. Tabletop centrifuge

> **Microfuge**: a small centrifuge that holds small 0.1 to 2 mL tubes; spins up to 14 krpm; commonly used for molecular biology experiments
>
> **Clinical centrifuge**: holds 5 to 15 mL tubes; spins at 1-5 krpm; used mostly in clinical labs

Floor model or tabletop centrifuge: holds large tubes from 1 to 50 mL; spins from 20 - 30 krpm; used in most cell and molecular biology labs

Ultracentrifuge: holds large tubes from 1 to 50 mL; spins up to 80 krpm; often refrigerated, sometimes equipped with a vacuum pump; the most expensive type, used only in some labs

3. Gel electrophoresis

This is used to fractionate DNA, RNA or protein molecules based on their size. The negative charges on the DNA or RNA make them migrate towards the anode (+) through tiny pores in the gel. The molecules migrate depending on their size and electric voltage in the system. Larger molecules move slowly and smaller molecules move fast. If the voltage is increased, the molecules move faster. Agarose gels are used to fractionate DNA or RNA. These are relatively easy to make but the size fractionation is approximate. Polyacrylamide gels are used to fractionate proteins and DNA sequencing reactions.

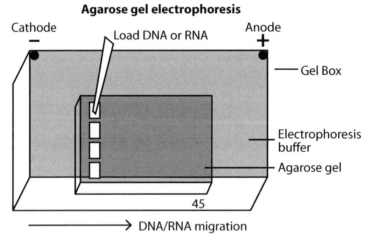

Figure 5-3. Gel electrophoresis

II. Overview of Cells

Prokaryotic and eukaryotic cells contain many different components and organelles that all have specialized functions. Within multicellular organisms, these cells may contain more of certain organelles or may be missing organelles entirely (e.g.: red blood cells lack nuclei).

Bacterial cells are among the simplest form of cell structures with a cell wall covering, plasma membrane surrounding the cytoplasm with all proteins, DNA, RNA and other molecules inside. Bacterial cells (prokaryotic) lack nucleus and all other membrane bound structures.

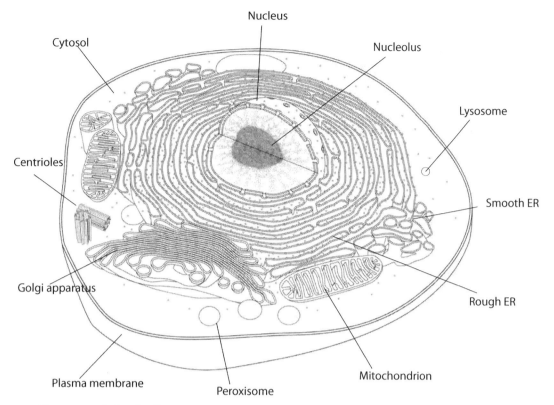

Cytosol

Nucleus

Nucleolus

Lysosome

Centrioles

Smooth ER

Golgi apparatus

Rough ER

Plasma membrane

Peroxisome

Mitochondrion

Figure 5-4. Animal cell

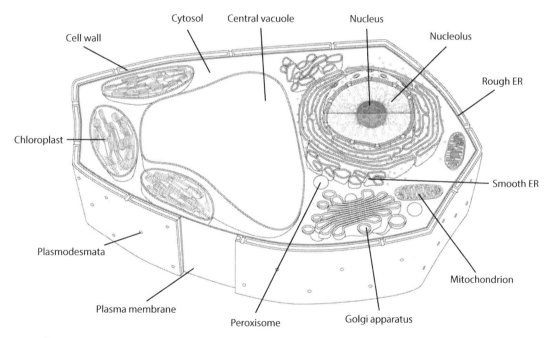

Cell wall

Cytosol

Central vacuole

Nucleus

Nucleolus

Rough ER

Chloroplast

Smooth ER

Plasmodesmata

Mitochondrion

Plasma membrane

Peroxisome

Golgi apparatus

Figure 5-5. Plant cell

Prokaryotic and eukaryotic cells

Prokaryotic	Eukaryotic
no nuclei, e.g.: bacteria	true nuclei, e.g.: plants, fungi, animals
DNA in the nucleoid region	DNA within nucleus
no proteins are attached to DNA	proteins (histones) are attached to DNA
no endomembrane system	vast endomembrane system
no organelles	membrane-bound organelles such as mitochondria and chloroplasts
cell size small, limited by metabolic requirements (mycoplasma 0.1- 1.0 μm, most bacteria 1-10 μm)	cell size much larger (10-100 μm) (10x in diameter, 100-600x in surface area and ~1000x in volume)

Major components of the eukaryotic cell

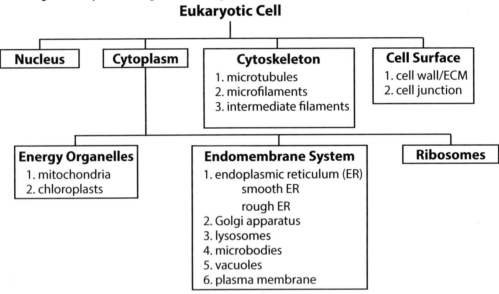

Figure 5-6. Concept map of cell components

Importance of compartments

Cells are very small in size and large eukaryotic cells are highly compartmentalized for the following reasons:

- provides greater surface area/volume ratio
- serves as partitions between different parts of the cell
- helps maintain unique lipid and protein composition
- enhances the range of metabolic functions
- provides localized environments for biochemical reactions
- sequesters reactions such as in respiration and photosynthesis

III. The Nucleus

The nucleus averages 5 μm as defined by a **nuclear membrane,** which surrounds the DNA loosely dispersed as **chromatin. Chromosomes** appear only during cell division. Proteins called **histones** bind DNA. The genes in nuclear DNA contain the programming for most cellular functions. DNA replication,

RNA synthesis (**transcription**) and RNA processing occur inside the nucleus.

Nucleolus is a region within nucleus that serves as organizing center for making ribosomes from ribosomal RNA and ribosomal proteins; contains about 20-30% of cellular RNA.

Nuclear pores present on membranes are approximately ~ 9 nm in diameter. These pores allow for movement of solutes in and out, for mRNAs to exit and for proteins to enter.

Nuclear lamina: a lining made of the protein laminarin inside the nuclear membrane.

Nuclear proteins: DNA polymerases (for **DNA replication**), RNA polymerases (for **transcription,** making RNA), DNA binding proteins (regulate transcription), RNA binding/processing proteins, small ribonucleoproteins, etc.

Nucleoplasm: the fluid inside the nucleus; a suspension of DNA, RNA, proteins, fibers, nucleotides, etc.

IV. Ribosomes

Ribosomes synthesize proteins with their catalytic ability. They are found freely in the cytoplasm (to make soluble proteins) or attached to the rough ER (to make membrane proteins). They are also found inside chloroplasts and mitochondria. Polysomes consist of several ribosomes bound to an mRNA, and they make proteins simultaneously.

A prokaryotic cell contains a few thousand ribosomes, and a eukaryotic cell contains a few million. Each ribosome is made up of one small subunit and one large subunit which contain different types of ribosomal RNA (rRNA) and proteins. Eukaryotic ribosomes:

Large subunit (28 S)   45 different proteins + 3 different rRNAs
Small subunit (18 S)   33 different proteins + 1 rRNA

The separate subunits of eukaryotic ribosomes are assembled in nucleolus region of nucleus. The small and large subunits come together only in the cytoplasm to begin protein synthesis (translation).

The ribosomes of bacteria and eukaryotes differ in the base sequence of their RNAs and proteins. As a result, antibiotics such as tetracycline and streptomycin inactivate bacterial ribosomes but not those of eukaryotes.

V. Endomembrane System

The components of the endomembrane system are interconnected with each other but the lipid and protein composition of the different components may be unique in each of them.

1. Endoplasmic reticulum (ER)

The ER is a network (reticulum) of membranes inside (endo) the cytoplasm (plasmic), like extended tubules or sacs with internal space called cisternae. There are two kinds of ER namely, smooth ER and rough ER. They are similar in structures except that the rough ER has ribosomes attached to it making them look "rough".

Smooth ER

- no ribosomes attached
- synthesizes lipids, i.e. fats, phospholipids and steroids (including hormones); abundant in testes and ovaries
- participates in carbohydrate metabolism; catalyzes glycogen to glucose reaction
- detoxifies unwanted chemicals including drugs; smooth ER content increases in persons addicted to drugs, requiring addicts to take increased dosage to get the same effect
- involves cytochrome P_{450} and other membrane-bound enzymes in drug detoxification
- stores Ca^{2+} necessary for muscle contractions; ER pumps Ca^{2+} from cisternae into cytosol to make muscles contract

Rough ER

- ribosomes attached for membrane protein synthesis
- synthesizes membrane-bound proteins for secretion and modification
- synthesizes membrane from phospholipids and membrane proteins

2. Golgi apparatus or Dictyosomes

- functions as the central receiving and dispatching center where proteins made in the ER arrive, are sorted out, packaged into vesicles and shipped to the target sites
- appears as flattened membrane sacs with cisternal space
- contains two sides: cis face for receiving proteins and a trans face for shipping proteins
- modifies proteins (e.g.: adds carbohydrates (glycosylation) or lipids (myristylation)) inside the cisternal space; contains enzymes to make oligosaccharides and add them to proteins
- Proteins shipped from vesicles to other parts of cell or excreted outside

3. Lysosomes

- membrane bags with hydrolytic enzymes (that come from the Golgi or ER) that can break down all four kinds of macromolecules
- acidic pH (5.0 compared to 7.4 on the outside) renders hydrolytic enzymes inactive outside the lysosomes
- digest food, microorganisms (phagocytosis) or organelles (autophagy)
- excretes digested material into cell if wanted or outside if not needed

Tay-Sachs disease is a genetic disease due to a lipid-digesting enzyme missing from lysosomes. The undigested lipids affect the brain.

4. Microbodies:

These are specialized metabolic organelles consisting of a compartment bound by a single membrane. They are found in both plant and animal cells

Peroxisomes
- are responsible for lipid degradation and detoxification of active oxygen species (O_2^-, OH^-, H_2O_2; highly reactive and mutagenic)
- contain enzymes
  - *peroxidase* which catalyzes $RH_2 + O_2 \longrightarrow R + H_2O_2$
  - *catalase* which catalyzes $2\,H_2O_2 \longrightarrow 2H_2O + O_2$

Glyoxysomes
- are specialized peroxisomes in plants that facilitates breakdown of storage lipids in germinating seeds that store large quantities of oils and lipids; the latter are converted into carbohydrates for the nourishment of growing seedlings

5. Vacuoles:

Large Central Vacuole
- present only in plant cells (increase in size as cell ages); plant vacuolar membrane is called the **tonoplast**
- stores organic compounds, inorganic ions such as K^+, Ca^{2+}, Cl^-, metabolic byproducts, waste products, lytic enzymes, pigments and water

Food Vacuoles
- helps primitive animals ingest food by endocytosis (engulfing into cell)
- fuses with lysosomes prior to digestion

Contractile Vacuoles
- in fresh water protists
- help remove excess water from the cell

VI. Energy Organelles

Mitochondria and chloroplasts are double-membrane organelles primarily important for the utilization and generation of carbohydrates, respectively.

Similarities between mitochondrion and chloroplast
- double membrane structure
- have their own DNA and proteins

- replicate autonomously
- import some proteins from the cytoplasm
- make ATP
- used for evolutionary studies

Differences between mitochondrion and chloroplast
- mitochondria found in all higher eukaryotes; chloroplasts found in plants only
- mitochondria perform respiration; chloroplasts perform photosynthesis and amino acid biosynthesis

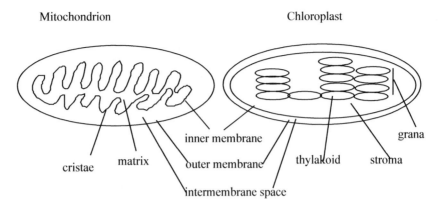

Figure 5-7. Mitochondrion and chloroplast

Plastids

Proplastid: premature plastids in seeds and embryos that matures into one of the following plastids.

Chloroplast: contains green and other color pigments and perform photosynthesis and amino acid biosynthesis.

Chromoplast: contains color pigments and may perform photosynthesis and amino acid biosynthesis or they simply store color pigments.

Leucoplast: colorless plastids that perform amino acid biosynthesis.

Amyloplast: starch-storing plastids

Endosymbiotic theory

The endosymbiotic theory has been proposed to explain how eukaryotic cells acquired chloroplasts and mitochondria. Curiously, chloroplasts and mitochondria have many features that are more prokaryotic than eukaryotic. They also have their own DNA and proteins and can replicate themselves.

According to the theory, early primitive eukaryotes engulfed bacteria or other prokaryotes that performed these energy-generating functions. The engulfed cells later evolved to become a permanent part of eukaryotic cells. However, this theory does not explain some other features of eukaryotic cells, such as the nucleus, import of cytoplasmic proteins into chloroplasts and mitochondria, and the process of cell division.

VII. Cytoskeleton

Three major types of cytoskeleton elements and their functions are listed in the following Table. Remember the monomers and all their functions.

In addition to the cytoskeleton elements, there are some proteins that help in mobility. These proteins attach themselves to microtubules and help in intracellular or cellular movement. Examples:

Dynein: attached to one set of microtubules and help in sliding on another set of microtubules; involved in ciliate and flagellate movement

Kinesin: helps in the movement of vesicles on the tracks of microtubules

Microtubules	Microfilaments	Intermediate filaments
Hollow tubes with walls containing 13 columns of tubulin protein	Solid rods of two inter-twined strands of actin.	Hollow tubes made up of heterogeneous proteins
25 nm with 15 nm lumen	7 nm	8-10 nm
Monomers, α-tubulin, β-tubulin	G actin and F actin	5 different proteins from the keratin family
present in all eukaryotic cells	actin in all eukaryotic cells, myosin only in animal cells	almost in all eukaryotic cells
1. cell motility (cilia, flagella, sperm) 2. cell shape 3. chromosome 4. serve as tracks for movement of organelles	1. cell motility (amoeboid movement using pseudopodia) 2. cell shape & change 3. muscle contraction 4. cytoplasmic streaming in plant cells 5. cleavage furrow	1. structural support 2. tensile strength 3. cell shape 4. anchoring the nucleus and other cell organelles 5. formation of nuclear lamina.

VIII. Cell Surface

1. Cell wall

Only found in bacteria, fungi, some protists and plants. Cell wall composition varies from kingdom to kingdom and also between major classes within a kingdom. Animal cells and many protists (amoeba, paramecium, rotifers) do not have cell walls. Some protsists such as microalgae and macroalage contain cell walls.

Plant cell walls
- contain polysaccharides such as **cellulose** (40-50%), **hemicellulose, cutin, pectin,** cell wall proteins etc.
- range in width from 0.1 to several μm
- protect cells, give physical support and help in water conservation
- layered: from outside the plant cell inwards, contain **middle lamella, primary cell wall, secondary cell wall and plasma membrane**
- cellulose can be degraded by the enzyme, **cellulase**

Young and annual plant cells contain mainly primary cell walls, which are thin and flexible. Older cells in herbaceous and woody plants contain primary and secondary cell walls, which are made up of the above components and lignin, suberin etc. that make it stronger by adding rigidity to its mechanical structure. Secondary cell walls form within the primary cell walls. The xylem elements in all plants consist of secondary cell wall growth. The layer between the neighboring cells is called middle lamella and contains the sticky polysaccharide pectin.

Fungi and some bacteria can make cellulase to digest plant cell walls. Animals do not have this enzyme. Ruminants harbor bacteria that make cellulase in their rumen to digest cellulose. Plant cell walls have pores called plasmodesmata which are important for cell to cell transport and viral movement.

Fungal cell walls

- contain **chitin** which is a b-1,4 linked **N-acetyl glucosamine (NAG)**
- chitin in fungal cell walls can be degraded by a plant enzyme called **chitinase** (a protective mechanism of plants against fungal infection); chitin is also present in insects' exoskeletons

Bacterial cell walls

- contain N-acetyl muramic acid and **N-acetyl glucosamine (NAM-NAG)**
- NAM-NAG linkage can be degraded by **lysozyme** present in our nasal secretions, tears and saliva (a protective mechanism against bacterial infection)

2. Animal Cell junctions

Animal cells do not have cell walls but have an **extracellular matrix (ECM)**, made up of glycoproteins and collagen fibers. Some glycoproteins at the cell surface are important for cell to cell signal transduction.

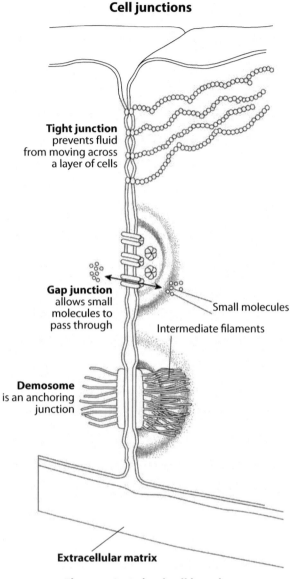

Cell junctions

Tight junction prevents fluid from moving across a layer of cells

Gap junction allows small molecules to pass through

Small molecules

Intermediate filaments

Demosome is an anchoring junction

Extracellular matrix

Figure 5-8. Animal cell junctions

Animal cells have three types of cell junctions:

Tight junction: two cell membranes are fused by integral membrane proteins to prevent movement of any solutes through the space between, e.g.: epithelial cells in stomach lining

Gap junctions: connections between two cells through connexons, channels through which chemical signals or solutes can pass from one cell to another; important for cell-to-cell communication

Desmosomes: spots where two cells are connected together by keratin-like fibrous proteins; contains cytoplasmic protein plaques (raised areas); not as tightly sealed as tight junctions, some space exists between two adjacent cells

6. BIOLOGICAL MEMBRANES

Concepts

- Cell membranes function as barriers, subdividing eukaryotic cells into compartments with unique chemical environments.
- The composition of these membranes affects their permeability to specific molecules.
- Small- and medium-sized molecules pass through biological membranes through active or passive processes.
- Macromolecules do not readily cross membranes, but there are specialized mechanisms for transport via endocytosis and exocytosis.

Outline

   I. Membrane Composition, Structure and Function
   II. Transport of Small Molecules
     (selective permeability, diffusion, active transport)
   III. Transport of Large Molecules
   IV. Other Functions of Membranes
     (metabolic reactions and signal transduction)

Biological membranes are the defining boundaries of cells and cell structures. They help in cellular transport; they are the place of many biochemical reactions; and they participate in cell signaling mechanisms.

1. Membrane Composition, Structure and Function

A. Composition

- Phospholipids are major components of the membrane. They are amphipathic in nature with hydrophobic tails and hydrophilic heads.
- Integral or intrinsic proteins traverse the membrane and peripheral or extrinsic proteins are bound to proteins on the surface.
- Other lipids such as cholesterol or carotenoids may be embedded in the membrane.
- Carbohydrates are found attached to lipids (glycolipids) or proteins (glycoproteins).

B. Structure

The Fluid Mosaic model is the currently accepted model proposed by Singer and Nicolson in 1972, based on freeze fracture studies of membranes. According to this model:
1. Membranes are not rigid static structures.
   - They are fluid and an integrated mosaic of several components such as lipids, proteins and carbohydrates.
   - Most lipids and some proteins can drift laterally through the membrane at about 2 μm per second.
2. The major force binding the membrane is hydrophobic interactions among the fatty acid side chains of phospholipids, other membrane

lipids and hydrophobic residues of the membrane proteins.
- Van der Waals forces also operate between the hydrocarbon chains of closely packed lipids.

3. The fluidity depends on the composition of the membranes (i.e. saturated vs. unsaturated fatty acids and cholesterol) and the temperature.
   - Unsaturation increases membrane fluidity and lowers melting temperature (T_m).
   - Saturation reduces membrane fluidity and increases the T_m.
4. Membranes are two-sided.
   - The cytoplasmic side is significantly different from the external side. This separation is critical for the functions of enzymes, receptors and transport proteins on the membrane.
   - The cytoplasmic side is interconnected with cytoskeleton elements for support and relative positioning of the membrane components.

C. Function

Membranes
1. form the boundaries of cells and their organelles.
2. are selectively permeable to facilitate transport.
3. allow many biochemical reactions to take place, either on the membrane itself or by providing the barriers needed to create separate chemical environments.
4. sequester many reactions and maintain unique local environments within the cell.
5. are critical for response to environmental changes, primarily by receiving and transmitting signals in signal transduction, which is important for cell-to-cell communication.

II. Transport of Small and Mediul Sized Molecules

The movement of small (1-100 Da, such as water, oxygen, CO_2, K^+ and Na^+ ions,) or medium-sized (101-1000 Da, such as glucose, sucrose and amino acids) molecules, both organic and inorganic depends on their size, charge and polarity. With respect to membrane permeability, a small or medium molecule is a relative term and small molecule may be the molecules smaller than 100 Daltons. A medium size molecule may be from 100 to 1000 Daltons; molecules larger than 1000 Daltons are referred to as large or macromolecules.

A. Selective permeability

Through the lipid portion of the bilayer:
- Hydrophobic molecules such as hydrocarbons, steroids, non-polar small molecules such as O_2 and CO_2, and small polar molecules such as water can easily pass through the lipid part of the bilayer.

Through transport proteins:
- Medium uncharged polar molecules such as glucose, charged ions (such as Na^+, Cl^-), and molecules (such as nucleotides or amino acids) cannot go through the lipid portion.

Specific membrane proteins facilitate the transport of charged ions and molecules across the membranes. These are also called ion channels. There are 3 types of transport proteins:

1. **Uniport:** Single solute, one direction, e.g.: H^+ pump
2. **Symport:** Two solutes, moving in one direction, e.g.: sucrose/H^+ pump
3. **Antiport:** Two solutes, moving in two opposite directions, e.g.: Na^+/K^+ pump

These transport proteins can be passive or active depending on their energy requirement.

Passive transport does not need cellular energy and the transport happens from high to low concentrations, i. e., down the concentration gradient.

Active transport requires energy in form of ATP, light or electrons. It transports against concentration gradient, from low to high concentrations.

B. Diffusion and passive transport

Diffusion is the tendency of molecules and ions to spread out in the available space until they reach equilibrium due to their thermal motion. The rate of diffusion is affected by the size of the molecule, temperature, electric charge and its concentration. Diffusion is passive, i.e.: from high to low concentration without using energy. Diffusion is important for the distribution of ions and other solutes within the cell. It takes a fraction of a millisecond for solutes to diffuse within a cell. There are two types of diffusion to cross the membrane barrier, osmosis and facilitated diffusion.

1. Osmosis

Osmosis is the diffusion of water from high concentration to low concentration through a selectively permeable membrane. Osmosis depends on the concentration of solutes (**osmoticum**) in the aqueous solution on the two sides separated by a semipermeable membrane. Solute concentration is related to osmotic pressure. If the solute concentration is higher, the osmotic pressure will be greater and the tendency to absorb water will be higher.

- **Hyperosmotic** *solution* (hypertonic): greater solute concentration.
- **Hypoosmotic** *solution* (hypotonic): lower solute concentration.
- **Isoosmotic** *solutions (*isotonic): the same concentration of solutes

All these terms are relative with reference to another solution.

Water moves from solutions with low solute concentration (i.e.: high water concentration) to high solute concentration (low water concentration). The effect of such water movement differs from cell to cell depending on the presence of cell wall.

External solution	Animal cells	Plant cells
Isotonic - same [solute]	stable	flaccid
Hypertonic - high [solute]	shrivel	plasmolyzed
Hypotonic - low [solute]	lysis	turgid

2. Facilitated Transport

Facilitated transport is the passive transport of molecules through an integral membrane protein specific for each type of solute. This includes the dffusion of charged solutes/ions (such as Na^+, Cl^- or amino acids) through transport proteins (ion channels).

- Transport is proportional to the solute concentration.
- Analogs (chemicals of similar structures) of the solute can block transport.
- Binding of solute changes conformation of the transport protein; once the solute is transported, the protein reverts to original conformation. E.g.: Cysteinuria, a genetic disorder with the cysteine transport protein missing. As a result, cysteine accumulates in urine causing kidney pain.

C. Active transport

Energy is used to transport solutes against the concentration gradient. This is the major force used to maintain internal concentrations of solutes and produce many biochemical reactions. Up to 40% of the cell's energy is used for active transport, e.g.: Na^+/K^+ pump. An intrinsic membrane protein uses one ATP to transport 3 Na^+ ions out of the cell and brings in 2 K^+ ions against their concentration gradient. Animal cells use this Na^+/K^+ pump on their plasma membrane to export Na^+ and import K^+ and maintain a net negative charge in side the cell as shown in Figure 6.1. Such pump is also referred to as antiport and electrogenic pump.

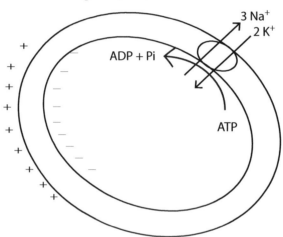

Figure 6-1. Active transport

The addition of a $-PO_4^-$ group (phosphorylation) changes the conformation of the Na^+/K^+ pump to facilitate the antiport function. After transport, it is dephosphorylated (phosphate removed) to gain back its original conformation.

Transport due to electric voltage difference

This is a form of active transport where electrochemical energy is the driving force for the active transport. **Voltage** is electric potential energy due to the separation of opposite charges. The **membrane potential** is the voltage across the membrane ranging from -50 to -200 mV (millivolts). The inside of the cell is more negative than the outside. The composition and concentration of charged ions such as Na^+, K^+, Cl^- determine the membrane potential. The **electrochemical gradient** is established from the combination of the membrane potential and the concentration gradient. Electrogenic pumps are the ion channels that drive the generation of membrane potential by transporting ions. Ions are transported from one side of the membrane to generate the electrochemical gradient, e.g. H^+ pump and Na^+/K^+ pump. Both make the outside more positive and inside more negative.

Coupled transport or Cotransport

This is also a form of active transport where a **primary active transport** (directly uses ATP for transport) system (e.g. H^+ pump) is coupled with another transport **secondary active transport** (e.g. H^+/glucose or H^+/amino acid) that does not use ATP but depends on the primary active transcport. Together, they are referred to as coupled transport or cotransport as shown in Figure 6.2 below.

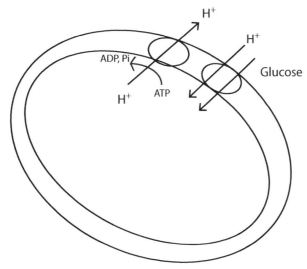

Figure 6-2. -Coupled transport

III. Transport of Large Molecules

Large molecules (larger than 1000 Daltons), such as proteins, starch, food particles or even whole cells, are transported by different mechanisms. These are active transport processes.

A. Exocytosis

Vesicles from the ER or Golgi bodies carrying macromolecules and other materials to be secreted fuse with the plasma membrane and open outside to secrete the materials. Examples:
1. In secretory cells, pancreatic hormones are secreted (e.g.: sweat glands, tear glands secrete bacteriolytic enzymes).
2. Plant cell wall materials, including proteins, are secreted.
3. Some viruses replicate inside the cell, are packaged in vesicles and get secreted outside without bursting the host cell.

B. Endocytosis

In addition to secretion, cells must also take up molecules or cells that are outside the cell, whether they are used for metabolism or need to be destroyed.
1. **Phagocytosis**: macrophage engulfing bacteria identified for destruction

2. **Pinocytosis** refers to cells gulping droplets of extracellular fluid.
3. **Receptor-mediated endocytosis**. Specific receptor proteins recognize large molecules such as cholesterol, change conformation and engulf low density lipoproteins containing several cholesterol molecules and related proteins into the cell for processing.

In addition to the above, the transport of the cytosolic proteins into chloroplasts and mitochondria is accomplished by signal sequence located at the amino terminus of the polypeptide. Specific proteins on the membranes recognize the signal sequence allowing them to be transported inside the above organelles. The transport of proteins from their site of synthesis to their target site is complex and utilize vesicles, cytoskeleton elements and motor proteins.

IV. Other Functions of Membranes

A. Biochemical reactions

Several biochemical reactions involved in respiration, photosynthesis, drug detoxification and biosynthesis of membrane proteins and lipids occur on the membrane structures. The energy transformation process needs charge separation (H^+s), as we will see in the respiration and photosynthesis chapters. Charge separations by the lipid portion of the bilayer and biochemical reactions by the integral and peripheral membrane proteins are critical for diverse functions.

B. Signal Transduction

In addition to performing transport and biochemical reactions, membranes perform the incredible task of sensing external cues and transmitting the signal inside the cell through various mechanisms (explained in detail in the next chapter). An extracellular molecule (the first messenger) binds to a receptor protein on the membrane which recognizes the particular ligand (a specific molecule or the functional group of a molecule); the receptor changes conformation, sends signals inside the cell through a second messenger (e.g. cAMP), which then transmits the message to another inside protein to start a cascade of reactions. Cells can respond to environmental signals by this mechanism. These signals can be communicated all the way to the genes in the nucleus, prompting them to synthesize new mRNAs to make new proteins in response to the situation.

7. CELL TO CELL COMMUNICATION

Concepts

- Cells communicate with their environment (including other cells), often by means of cell surface proteins.
- External signals can elicit changes that permeate the cell.
- Adjacent cells may communicate directly with each other through cell-cell junctions.
- Signal transduction pathways can lead to gene expression.
- Almost all cells in an organism contain the same genes, but cells differentiate and specialize as a result of the genes they express.

Outline

I. Overview of Cell Signaling
II. Signal Reception
III. Signal Transduction
IV. Cellular Response

1. Overview of Cell Signaling

Cell communication is an important process that occurs from the beginning to the end of a cell's life cycle.

Why do cells need to communicate?

The reasons for cell communication can be broadly grouped into the following categories. Some are interrelated.

1. **Recognition:** Cells need to recognize neighboring cells and surfaces.
2. **Reproduction:** Cells and organisms send and receive reproductive cues.
3. **Response to stimuli:** Individual cells and organisms can respond to different types of environmental stimuli such as light, touch, gravity etc.
4. **Growth and development:** Growth and development of multicellular organisms require a coordinated effort by millions or billions of cells.
5. **Survival and defense mechanisms:** Sensors on the cell surface can recognize potential dangers, triggering the cell to make defense proteins.
6. **Metabolic functions:** Most metabolic functions are internal to cells and highly coordinated, making cells effective and efficient.
7. **Movement:** At the organismal level, movement is a response due to a stimulus or signal received from the central nervous system.
8. **Adaptation to the environment:** This cumulative result of several signaling pathways over a period of time can maintain the temperature of internal ion concentrations.

Where does the communication occur?

1. **Intracellular communication:** occurs within the cell itself, i.e. in the cytoplasm, the nucleus, or between the cytoplasm and other organelles.
2. **Intercellular communication:** occurs between cells located close to or

far away from each other; signals are secreted through gap junctions or communicated by the cell surface proteins on the plasma membrane of the signaling cell to the receptors on another cell located close by (local or **paracrine signaling**) or from the endocrine cells to cells located far away (e.g. hormonal or **endocrine signaling**). The signaling between nerve cells involves **synaptic signaling**.

3. **Between organisms**: occurs between two unicellular or multicellular organisms; complex multicellular organisms have various types of signal communication mechanisms depending on their sensory organ systems.

How do cells communicate and what are the components involved?

First, signaling molecules such as hormones, proteins, ions and other chemical signals must be present nearby or generated by the cell. Such signals are called *first messengers*. Some signals are external cues such as light or gravity. After the first messenger is generated, cell communication can be analyzed in 3 stages, namely, (1) signal reception, (2) signal transduction and (3) cell response.

1. **Signal reception:** The first messenger can be recognized by specific receptors (e.g.: integral membrane proteins or enzymes). The signal activates the receptor which activates the signaling pathway inside the cell.

2. **Signal transduction:** Inside the cell, the signal is converted by activating another protein which may activate yet another protein and start a cascade of signaling pathways. In this process a chemical such as cAMP (adenosine monophosphate) or inositol phosphate are generated. These compounds are called *second messengers*.

3. **Cellular response:** Once the signaling pathway is activated, the cell or organism responds through increased gene expression and metabolic activity, growth, defense and movement.

II. Signal Receptors

There are four major groups of signal receptors. Among these, the first three are membrane proteins and the 4th group includes soluble proteins. Here we will discuss only the details of G-protein linked receptors.

G-protein linked receptors recognize signals and then act through a GTP-binding protein known as G-protein. This binding activates an enzyme to make an internal second messenger which will cause the cellular response. G-protein linked receptors are similar in their structure but vary in their specificity to different signals. These receptors are involved in embryonic development, vision and taste. Many bacterial diseases such as cholera, botulism and pertussis affect the G-protein linked signaling system and about 60% of modern medicines act through G-protein linked signaling pathways.

Other membrane protein receptors include Tyrosine Kinase Receptors and Ion Channel Receptors. Intracellular Receptors are soluble proteins in the cytoplasm or the nucleus, specifically for certain soluble chemicals or lipid-soluble hormones that can pass through the membrane easily. These signals bind to receptors in the cytoplasm, which are then activated to become DNA-binding proteins that initiate the transcription of specific genes.

III. Signal Transduction

Signal transduction refers to the process of translating and communicating signals recognized by receptors. The signal transduction pathway may involve one or more of the following mechanisms.

Phosphorylation Cascade

The binding of the first messenger to the receptor results in the phosphorylation of the receptor itself or the proteins/enzymes associated with the receptors. Phosphorylation is catalyzed by kinase's removal of phosphates – dephosphorylation is catalyzed by phosphatases. This is a common mode of activating several enzymes in a phosphorylation cascade for a rapid response to a signal. For example, the blood-clotting response triggered by an injury is rapidly activated by phosphorylation cascade.

Second Messenger System

Second messengers such as cAMP or Ca^{++} are sometimes used to relay signals inside. The binding of a ligand/signal (first messenger) activates a receptor which in turn activates a G-protein or another protein nearby. This activates an enzyme that makes cAMP from ATP or releases Ca^{++} inside the cell from the ER. The increased Ca^{++} concentration causes various cellular responses.

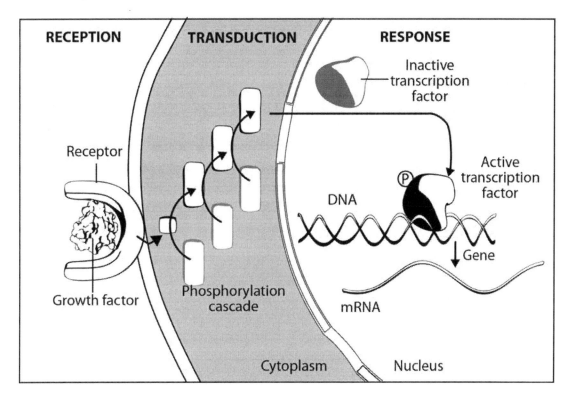

Figure 7-1. Cellular response to growth factor

IV. Cellular Response

The ultimate purpose of cell communication is to elicit a response from the cell at various levels. The response is sometimes amplified many-fold during signal transduction by one protein activating many proteins, which in turn activate more proteins. For example, the binding of epinephrine hormones to a G-protein linked receptor will result in a million enzymes that will phosphorylate over 100 million glucose molecules leading to the massive amount of ATP synthesis needed during a stress response.

The response may occur at the molecular level (DNA expression or protein synthesis and activity), the cellular level (metabolic activity, cytoskeletal organization, cell movement) or the organismal level (fight or flight response).

Many signal transduction pathways are targeted to specific receptors, which in turn will activate specific proteins adjacent to them. Two or more signal transduction pathways operate simultaneously in the cell, which regulates the specific response needed for the situation.

BIG IDEA 2

FLOW OF ENERGY

Biological systems survive, grow and change by processes based upon chemical transformation pathways and are governed by the laws of thermodynamics.

Chapters

8. Metabolism
9. Respiration
10. Photosynthesis

8. INTRODUCTION TO METABOLISM

Concepts

- Biological systems follow the laws of physics and chemistry.
- Free energy concepts explain the spontaneity of biochemical and other reactions.
- Enzymes are the molecular machines that operate biological processes.
- Enzymes are affected by various factors and their activity is regulated by different mechanisms.

Outline

I. Concepts of energy
II. ATP and cellular work
III. Enzymes and catalysts

One of the main properties of a living cell is **metabolism**. Metabolism, referring to the sum of all biochemical reactions that take place in an organism, is what makes and sustains cells. Metabolic reactions produce and break down organic molecules, providing cellular energy for cells to move, transport and do a variety of actions. Synthetic or constructive biochemical reactions are **anabolic** processes, and degradative biochemical reactions are **catabolic** processes. **Catalysis** means a biochemical reaction facilitated by an enzyme for conversion of reactants into products. In this chapter we will study the basic concepts of energy, ATP (adenosine triphosphate), enzymes and enzyme regulation.

Metabolism
Anabolic
catabolic
catalysis

1. Concepts of Energy

Energy: capacity to do work, expressed in kcal/mol or kJoules/mol (1 kcal = 4.18 kJ); there are different forms of mechanical energy.
Kinetic energy: due to motion of molecules or objects
- Heat is a form of kinetic energy due to the movement of molecules.
- Light is a form of kinetic energy in the form of photons moving from one place to another at a particular speed.

Potential energy: due to position, location or arrangement
- An object in an elevated place has potential energy.
- Molecules have potential energy in their bonds. This again is due to the position of electrons spinning in different orbits.

Energy
kinetic Ener
Potential Ener

Thermodynamics

The study of heat and its transformation to mechanical energy is called **thermodynamics**.

First law of thermodynamics: Energy can be transferred or transformed, but it cannot be created or destroyed, i.e.: the total energy of the universe is constant.
Second law of thermodynamics: Energy transfer or transformation leads to increased disorder or randomness in the universe.

Thermodynamics
1st Law
2nd Law
Entropy

A situation or an object may be a **closed system**, where matter cannot enter or leave while energy is exchanged with the external surroundings, or an **open system**, where both energy and matter are free to enter or leave the system. All biological organisms are open systems exchanging energy, air, food and other materials with the outside surroundings. The universe is considered to be a true closed system with constant matter and energy. For practical purposes, a refrigerator can be considered a closed system as matter can remain constant while energy can enter or exit.

Entropy is a measure of randomness denoted by ΔS, where Δ denotes a change, i.e. condition at the time observed minus initial condition. **Enthalpy** is the heat content or the total potential energy denoted by ΔH. **Free energy** is the portion of a system's energy that is available to perform work when the temperature is uniform throughout the system; an expression combining the entropy and enthalpy denoted by ΔG. The relationship between free energy, entropy and enthalpy is expressed by the equation $\Delta G = \Delta H - T\Delta S$, where T = absolute temperature in K (Kelvin = °C + 273).

If the ΔG is negative, it is considered a spontaneous, downhill or favorable (thermodynamically) reaction; if it is positive, it is considered a non-spontaneous, uphill or an unfavorable reaction.

In terms of free energy release or use, we can group reactions as **exergonic**, net release of free energy ($-\Delta G$), or **endergonic**, net absorption of free energy ($+\Delta G$).

Examples of spontaneous reactions are ice melting at room temperature and a ball rolling down a slope. Examples of non-spontaneous reactions are climbing uphill and cooling water at room temperature.

Spontaneous reactions are favored by
1. decrease in enthalpy ($-\Delta H$),
2. increase in entropy ($+\Delta S$),
3. decrease in free energy ($-\Delta G$) and
4. increase in temperature (T).

However, it is the combination of changes in enthalpy, temperature and entropy that will decide if a reaction will be endergonic or exergonic.

Chemical reaction

Chemical bond energy is the amount of energy consumed to break a chemical bond or the amount of energy released when such a bond is formed. For example, some bond energies are given below.

Bond	C-C	C-H	C-O	C=O	O-H	O=O
Energy(kcal/mol)	83	99	84	174	111	118

Based on the net result of a reaction in terms of heat release or absorption, we can call a reaction
Exothermic: heat is released ($-\Delta H$), e.g.: burning of methane gas
Endothermic: heat is absorbed ($+\Delta H$), e.g.: dissolving urea in water

We can summarize the free energy changes as follows:

HIGHER ENERGY STATE
eg. glucose, $C_6H_{12}O_6$

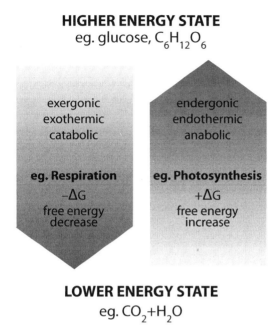

exergonic
exothermic
catabolic

eg. Respiration
$-\Delta G$
free energy
decrease

endergonic
endothermic
anabolic

eg. Photosynthesis
$+\Delta G$
free energy
increase

LOWER ENERGY STATE
eg. $CO_2 + H_2O$

Figure 8-1. Free energy changes

Chemical equilibrium is the balance between forward and reverse reactions. At equilibrium the concentrations of reactants and products remain constant as measured by K_{eq} (*equilibrium constant*). K_{eq} is known as the ratio of the concentration of products over the concentration of reactants at equilibrium. e.g.: for the reaction A + B (reactants) -------> C + D (products)

$$Keq = [C] \times [D] / [A] \times [B]$$

The higher K_{eq}, the faster the reaction occurs. Two examples:

    1. Fructose 6-P → Glucose 6-P
    $K_{eq} = 2.0$
    $\Delta G = -0.4$

    2. Sucrose + water → Fructose + Glucose
    $K_{eq} = 140,000$
    $\Delta G = -7.0$

From these numbers we can tell that the second reaction is happening much faster, and it is more favorable than the first reaction. In other words, Keq indicates how many products are being made at the state of equilibrium for each reactant remaining in the reaction. The changes in ΔG is not proportional to the changes in Keq and vice versa. There is a general tendency that reactions with high Keq values will tend to be highly spontaneous.

11. ATP and Cellular Work

Living cells perform three major kinds of work by using ATP.
1. Mechanical work: e.g., movement of cilia or flagella
2. Active transport: e.g., Na^+/K^+ pump
3. Chemical reactions: some metabolic reactions that need energy, e.g., sucrose biosynthesis.

The structure of ATP is shown on the next page. The bonds (~) between the phosphate groups in ATP are considered high-energy bonds due to the net release of free energy during hydrolysis. They are fragile because of the clustering of negative charges of oxygen attached to the three phosphorus atoms. They have a tendency to hydrolyze in the presence of water at room temperature. So ATP is unstable at room temperature and needs to be stored under deep freezing condition for long term storage. Hydrolysis of ATP at room temperature is shown below.

$$ATP + H_2O \longrightarrow ADP + P_i \text{ (inorganic phosphate)}$$

The ΔG of this reaction is -7.3 kcal/mol (*in vitro*), with a net release of free energy, making it an exergonic or spontaneous reaction. It is much greater (-12 kcal/mol) under *in vivo* conditions.

ATP and energy coupling

Since ATP hydrolysis is a thermodynamically favorable exergonic reaction, it can be coupled with endergonic reactions that are not spontaneous. For example, the reaction Glucose + Fructose → Sucrose + H_2O (ΔG = + 6.5 kcal/mol) is not spontaneous because of + ΔG, so an ATP is used to drive this reaction forward. To make this reaction spontaneous, ATP is used initially to phosphorylate glucose, which is then combined with fructose to make sucrose.

$$\text{Glucose + ATP} \rightarrow \text{Glucose-P + ADP} \quad \text{(-7.3 kcal/mol)}$$
$$\text{Glucose-P + Fructose} \rightarrow \text{Sucrose} + P_i. \text{ (+ 6.5 Kcal/mol)}$$

ΔG for this coupled reaction is – 0.8 kcal/mol.

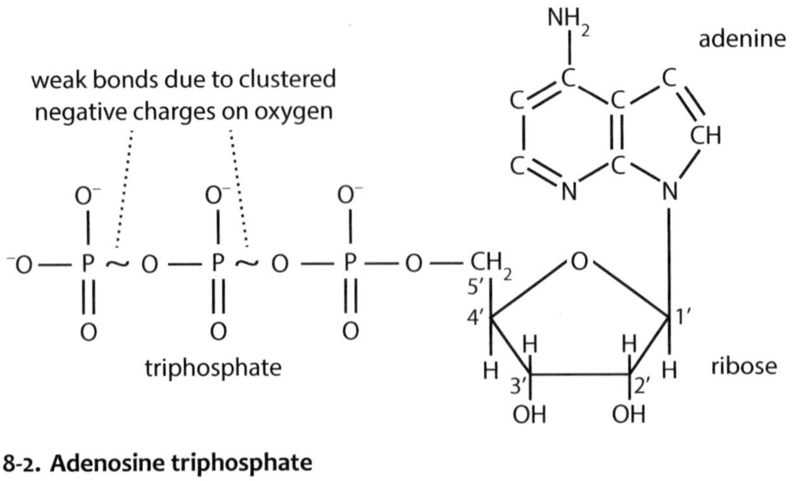

Figure 8-2. Adenosine triphosphate

Addition of a -P group ($-OPO_3^-$) to a molecule or protein is called phosphorylation, as we have seen before in Na^+/K^+ pump. The enzymes catalyzing phosphorylation reactions are generally called kinases. ATP synthesis occurs in the cytoplasm, mitochondria and chloroplasts, as we will see in detail in the chapters on respiration and photosynthesis. ATP synthesis is an endergonic process as shown below.

$$ADP + P_i \rightarrow ATP + H_2O (\Delta G = +7.3 \text{ kcal/mol})$$

ATP is constantly made and utilized. A cell does not store a stockpile of ATP but maintains a high ATP/ADP ratio. A working muscle cell makes and uses approximately 10 million ATP molecules per second.

III. Enzymes and Catalysts

A. Activation energy

Enzymes are biological catalysts. Before a reaction occurs, energy must be consumed to break the bonds. This initial priming of energy is called free energy of activation (E_a). This is similar to starting a car with the ignition or using the pilot lamp to light a gas stove. Enzymes do not change the free energy in a reaction (ΔG), but they accelerate the reaction by lowering the free energy of activation. This is accomplished by some functional groups such as -SH, -OH, $-NH_2$ or $-COO^-$ on the side chains of the enzymes.

Enzymes have a high specificity for a particular *substrate* (a reactant used by an enzyme), determined by the physical conformation and the amino acid side chains of the *active site* (the site of an interaction between an enzyme and its substrate). The enzyme recognizes the substrate by its molecular shape and functional group(s). The enzyme conformation changes to embrace the substrate and to act on it. This is called **induced fit.**

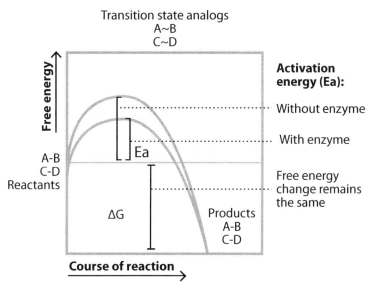

Figure 8-3. Change in activation energy due to enzyme

B. Factors affecting enzyme activity

1. *Temperature*: Each enzyme has an optimum temperature for maximum activity. The optimum temperature for enzymes in humans is 37°C, and that for the enzymes in a thermophilic bacteria is 72°C.
2. *pH*: Similar to temperature, enzymes require an optimum pH condition to operate, e.g.: the optimum pH for pepsin in stomach acid is 2.0 and for trypsin in saliva is 8.0.
3. *Salt*: In addition to optimum temperature and pH, enzymes require the presence of certain ions or salts at certain concentrations to catalyze reactions, e.g.: DNA polymerase needs Mg^{2+} for making DNA polymers.
4. *Substrate*: An enzyme needs the right kind of substrate(s) to perform the reaction.

V_{max} is the highest velocity of the enzyme (maximum rate of reaction). V_{max} is achieved when all the enzyme active sites are filled with the substrate (i.e.:saturated). The rate of reaction varies with the substrate concentration [S], pH, temperature and ionic strength. It is measured by K_m.

K_m is the substrate concentration at which the rate of the reaction is half its maximum, i.e: the [S] at which half the enzyme active sites are filled with substrates. Each enzyme has a specific V_{max} and K_m for each substrate. Depending on the substrate, the K_m for an enzyme varies from 10^{-1} to 10^{-7} M.

Cofactors or *prosthetic groups* help activate enzymes. Prosthetic groups can be inorganic or organic and they participate in the reaction by accepting or donating electrons.
- *Inorganic cofactors*: Zn, Fe, Cu.
- *Organic cofactors*: Coenzyme A, NAD^+, FAD, $NADP^+$.

C. How do enzymes work?

Enzymes recognize their substrates by their molecular shape and functional groups, and change their conformation (induced fit) to fit the substrate and make contacts. **Carboxypeptidase** (shown in Figure 8.4) is a protease (a protein degrading enzyme) that can recognize the carboxyl terminus of a protein (substrate), make close bonds with the substrate and perform hydrolysis of the last amino acid at the carboxyl terminus. During hydrolysis, several interactions occur between the active site and the substrate.

Carboxypetidase

Carboxypetidase cleavage site

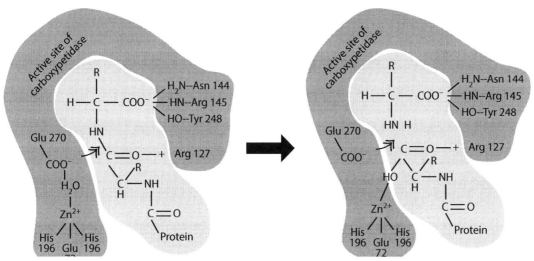

Figure 8-4. Interaction between the active site of carboxypeptidase and the substrate

Contact between the substrate and the active site of the enzyme may be an ionic interaction, H-bonding, van der Waals interaction or even covalent bonding to make the transition state analog stable and to allow the enzyme to perform its catalytic function. This interaction at the molecular level makes the reaction spontaneous (-ΔG) and reduces the activation energy (E_a).

D. Regulation of enzyme activity:

1. Activators and Inhibitors

Activators bind to the enzyme, changing its conformation with a positive effect on its activity. **Inhibitors**, on the other hand, do the opposite by binding to the enzyme and changing its conformation, resulting in a reduced enzyme activity. There are three types of inhibitors:

- **Competitive inhibitors** compete with the substrate for the same active site on the enzyme. These are usually analogs (similar molecules) with different functional groups, e.g.: oxaloacetate is a competitive inhibitor of succinate dehydrogenase which catalyzes succinate ßà fumarate reaction. This is reversible. In the case of a competitive inhibitor, a higher concentration of the substrate can be added to overcome the competition. Thus the V_{max} is not altered but the K_m increases.

- **Non-competitive inhibitors** bind to the protein at some place other than the active site, changing the conformation of an enzyme and making it less active or inactive. Adding more of the substrate does not overcome the inhibition. So V_{max} decreases and K_m remains the same, e.g.: DDT. This is also reversible.

- **Irreversible inhibitors** bind to the active site and make the enzyme permanently inactive, e.g. penicillin binds to a bacterial cell wall synthesizing enzyme and cyanide binds to a respiratory protein and irreversibly inactivates them. Irreversible inhibition is mostly terminal and it is not employed for regulation.

2. Allosteric regulation

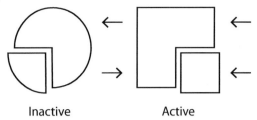

Inactive   Active

Figure 8-8. Conformational change in allosteric enzyme

'Allo' means alternate and 'steric' means conformation or shape. These enzymes have active and inactive forms. The following features characterize allosteric enzymes.

- They are complex enzymes with separate catalytic (binding to substrate) and regulatory (binding to activator or inhibitor) subunits (two or more proteins attached).
- An activator or inhibitor binds to the enzyme and changes its conformation to an active or an inactive form, respectively.
- They respond to the substrate concentration in a sigmoidal fashion.

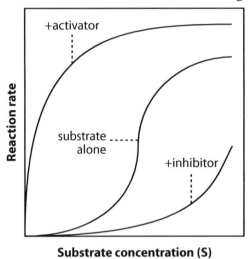

Figure 8-9. Effect of activators and inhibitor on allosteric enzyme activity

- The binding of an activator results in cooperative changes in conformation of the entire enzyme. This is known as cooperativity.

3. Feedback regulation

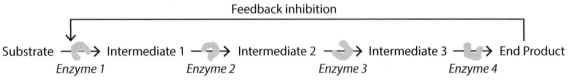

Figure 8-10.   **End product of a metabolic pathway inhibits a key regulatory enzyme**

The end product of a biosynthetic pathway or an intermediate of another related pathway inhibits an earlier enzyme and stops the whole pathway, e.g. the end products valine, leucine and isoleucine inhibit the first key regulatory enzyme acetolactate synthase in the branched chain amino acid biosynthetic pathway.

4. Chemical modification

Some of the enzymes or proteins are chemically modified by themselves or by other enzymes to make them active or inactive. The chemical modification may involve adding a functional group such as a phosphate to the regulatory subunit of the enzyme, e.g., **phosphorylation** by **kinases** make an enzyme or ion channel protein active or inactive, e.g., Na+-K+ pump. Phosphorylation by kinases can add a phosphate to serine, threonine or tyrosine amino acids in a protein. Due to the negative charge of phosphate group, the enzyme conformation changes and it results in either activation or inactivation. There are enzymes called phosphatases that can remove the phosphates.

This chapter covered the major concepts of energy transformations, ATP structure and enzyme activity. There will be specific examples of enzymes and ATP use in the next chapters on respiration and photosynthesis.

9. RESPIRATION

Concepts

- Oxidation of organic compounds drives the processes of respiration and fermentation.
- ATP is made in multiple stages including glycolysis, Krebs cycle and oxidative phosphorylation.
- Electron carriers and organic cofactors such as NAD^+ and FAD are essential for transferring electrons from organic molecules through various processes to make ATP.
- Oxygen is the ultimate acceptor of electrons, driving the oxidation process of organic compounds in respiration.
- In the absence of oxygen, anaerobic fermentation forms small amounts of ATP and lactate or ethanol as byproducts.

Outline

I. Basic Reactions
II. Glycolysis
III. Acetyl CoA Formation
IV. Krebs Cycle
V. Oxidative Phosphorylation
VI. Anaerobic Respiration and Fermentation

Respiration is essential for life to generate ATP and various organic compounds from energy storage compounds. Respiration is defined as an aerobic process wherein oxygen is consumed to break down carbohydrates, fats or proteins to generate ATP and two major by-products: water and carbon dioxide. In the absence of oxygen, cells carry out fermentation that utilizes only carbohydrates and generate small amounts of ATP.

I. Basic Reactions

A. Respiration

A basic, simplified and general equation for aerobic respiration is as follows:

$$\text{glucose} + \text{oxygen} \rightarrow \text{carbon dioxide} + \text{water} + \text{energy}$$
$$C_6H_{12}O_6 + 6O_2 \rightarrow 6CO_2 + 6\,H_2O + {\sim}30\text{-}32\ \text{ATP}$$

Respiration occurs in 4 major processes in different locations inside cell.

1. Glycolysis — *cytoplasm*
2. Acetyl CoA formation — *mitochondria*
3. Krebs cycle — *primarily in the matrix*
4. Oxidative phosphorylation — *inner membrane of mitochondria*

Respiration can utilize energy compounds (carbohydrates, fats and proteins) each entering at different steps to generate ATP.

B. Reduction - Oxidation (redox) reactions

Many reactions that occur in the cell involve reduction and oxidation. Reduction is gain of electrons or loss of oxygen. Oxidation on the other hand is gain of oxygen or loss or electrons. Remember the saying "OIL RIG" which refers to oxidation is loss and reduction is gain of electrons.

Examples
1.

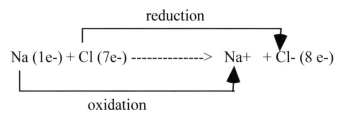

Na : reducing agent - donates e-.

Cl : oxidizing agent - accepts e-.

Figure 9-1. Reduction oxidation during salt formation (NaCl)

2.

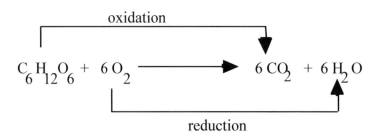

$C_6H_{12}O_6$: reducing agent (donates hydrogen / electrons)

O_2 : oxidizing agent (accepts hydrogen / electrons)

Figure 9-2. Reduction oxidation during respiration

The above reaction represents respiration, which is an oxidation process. The electrons extracted from the food molecules are ultimately lost to oxygen to generate ATP.

C. Electron carriers

Since electrons are very reactive, there are specific electron carriers, NAD^+ and FAD, that help in transporting electrons within the cell. The electron carriers must be regenerated to accept electrons to keep the respiration or fermentation process going.

1. NAD+ (Nicotinamide Adenine Dinucleotide)
This is one of the important electron carriers in respiration, transferring the electrons gained in the oxidation of glucose and a few other molecules to the electron transport system to drive ATP synthesis.

- One positive charge
- Can carry two electrons and one proton

The NADHs inside mitochondria transfer electrons at a high energy level resulting in approximately 3 ATPs per NADH. There are separate pools of NAD^+ and NADH in the cytoplasm and mitochondria.

$$NAD^+ + 2\,H \xrightarrow{\text{reduction}} NADH + H^+$$

$$NADH \xrightarrow{\text{oxidation}} NAD^+ + 2\,e^- + H^+$$

NAD^+ : oxidizing agent (accepts e^-)
NADH : reducing agent (donates e^-)

Figure 9-3. Reduction oxidation of electron carrier NAD^+

2. FAD (Flavo Adenine Dinucleotide)

This is another electron carrier in respiration involved in transferring electrons from the citric acid cycle to the electron transport system to drive ATP synthesis.

- Accepts two electrons and two protons

$FADH_2$ operates within mitochondria. It transfers electrons at a lower energy level than NADH, resulting in approximately 2 ATPs made per $FADH_2$.

$$FAD + H_2 \rightarrow FADH_2$$
$$FADH_2 \rightarrow FAD + 2\,e^- + 2\,H^+$$

D. ATP synthesis

ATP is made in two ways during respiration, namely, substrate-level phosphorylation and oxidative phosphorylation.

Substrate level phosphorylation: Synthesis of ATP by transferring a phosphate from a high-energy phosphate compound to ADP (adenosine diphosphate) by enzymes known as kinases. This process, which occurs during glycolysis in the cytoplasm, generates a limited amount of ATPs. This is the only process to generate ATPs in anaerobic fermentation.

For example: Phosphoenolpyruvate + ADP à Pyruvate + ATP.

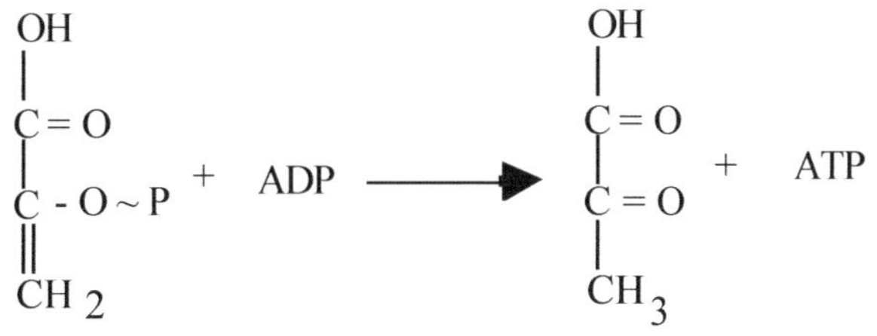

PEP   Pyruvate

Figure 9-4. Substrate level phosphorylation

Oxidative phosphorylation: This is the major aerobic process to generate ATPs for cellular energy. This occurs in mitochondria of eukaryotic cells, specifically in the inner membrane and the intermembrane space. In prokaryotes, it occurs on the plasma membrane.

This process is best explained by the chemiosmotic theory proposed by Peter Mitchell.

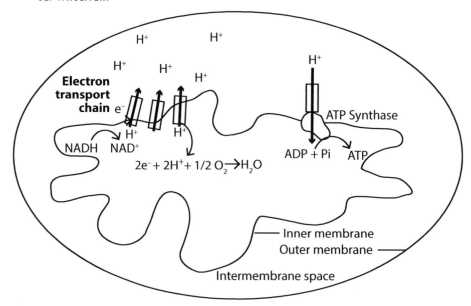

Figure 9-5. Oxidative phosphorylation

According to this hypothesis, NADH or $FADH_2$ electron carriers transfer the electrons stripped from food molecules. These electrons are then transferred through a series of membrane proteins known as the **electron transport chain** and are finally accepted by O_2. During this electron transfer process, H^+s are pumped from the matrix into the intermembrane space of mitochondria generating a $[H^+]$ gradient. In addition, the concentration of positive charges in the intermembarne space (due to high concetration of H^+) and negative charges (due to low concetration of H^+) in matrix results in electrochemical gradient. The membrane protein complex ATP-synthase generates ATP by combining ADP with an inorganic phosphate (P_i). When the H^+s return into matrix through ATP synthase they release the tightly bound ATP. The H^+s returning to the matrix due to their concentration gradient is called **proton motive force**.

Aerobic respiration occurs in a series of processes as shown in the next pages.

11. Glycolysis

Glycolysis refers to the break down (lysis) of sugar (glyco). It is the most primitive pathway to oxidize food to generate energy. It occurs in the cytoplasm in two phases.

1. Energy investment phase (5 steps) during which glucose is broken down into two trioses with an investment of 2 ATP.
2. Energy-yielding phase (5 steps) results in 4 total and 2 net ATP, 2 pyruvate, and 2 NADH.

Overall pathway of glycolysis is shown in the Figure 9.6.

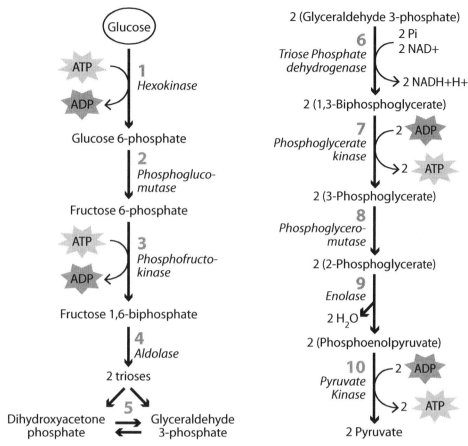

Figure 9-6. Glycolysis

Energy-investment phase

Step 1. Glucose is phosphorylated by hexokinase, made of hexose (a 6 -C sugar) + kinase (a phosphorylating enzyme). Mg^{2+} is needed in this first priming event (energy investing) which uses the first ATP. This is also the first committed step for glycolysis, meaning once this step is completed it must continue through the whole process.

Glucose + ATP → Glucose 6-phosphate + ADP

Once the glucose is phosphorylated and negatively charged, it is reactive and does not leave the cell. If the cell needs of ATP, glucose is used for glycolysis. Excess accumulation of glucose 6-phosphate can inhibit the hexokinase from phosphorylating more glucose molecules.

Step 2. Glucose 6-phosphate is converted to fructose 6-phosphate. This step is an aldose → ketose conversion by phosphoglucoisomerase to prepare for another phosphorylation.

Glucose 6-phosphate → Fructose 6-phosphate

Step 3. Phosphorylation of fructose 6-phosphate by Phosphofructokinase

(PFK; a kinase which phosphorylates a phospho-fructose). This enzyme also needs Mg^{2+}. *This is the key regulatory step (the second energy-investing step) and an important step to remember.*

Fructose 6-phosphate + ATP → Fructose 1,6-bisphosphate + ADP

Phosphofructokinase (PFK) is the key regulatory enzyme, meaning it can make glycolysis go faster, slower or stop. This is a complex allosteric enzyme. It is induced by high levels of ADP or AMP (means the cell needs ATP) and inhibited by high levels of ATP (means the cell has enough ATP) and citrate (the first committed product of Krebs cycle, another indication of cells having enough ATP).

Step 4. Fructose 1,6-bisphosphate is split into two trioses by aldolase. The fructose ring opens and aldolase splits fructose 1,6-bisphosphate in the middle into two trioses.

Fructose 1,6-bisphosphate →
Dihydroxyacetonephosphate + Glyceraldehyde 3-phosphate

Step 5. Reversible conversion of two trioses by triosephosphate isomerase.

Dihydroxyacetonephosphate + Glyceraldehyde 3-phosphate

Dihydroxyacetonephosphate and glyceraldehyde 3-phosphate are structural isomers. The equilibrium is towards glyceraldehyde 3-phosphate because it is utilized by the next 5 steps of glycolysis rapidly.

In the above set of 5 reactions, 2 ATPs have been invested per glucose.

Energy-yielding phase

The following 5 reactions will yield 4 ATPs per glucose. Since each of the trioses in step 5 will undergo these reactions there will be two such reactions from step 6 through step 10, for each glucose.

Step 6. Oxidation of Glyceraldehyde 3- Phosphate (G_3P) and phosphorylation to generate 1,3-bisphosphoglycerate (BPG) by triose phosphate dehydrogenase.

One proton (H^+) and two electrons are removed (oxidation) from G_3P and another low energy phosphate (inorganic phosphate) is added at the 1st C to generate 1,3 BPG. The electrons and proton are transferred to NAD^+ (oxidizing agent), which gets reduced to NADH. NADH transfers electrons to the electron transport chain to generate ATP inside mitochondria.

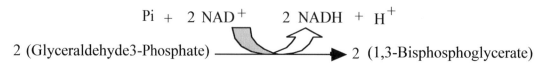

$$Pi + 2\ NAD^+ \qquad 2\ NADH + H^+$$

2 (Glyceraldehyde3-Phosphate) ⟶ 2 (1,3-Bisphosphoglycerate)

Triose phosphate dehydrogenase

The enzyme triose phosphate dehydrogenase is a complex enzyme which can perform both oxidation and phosphorylation simultaneously. The presence of an -SH group in its active sites helps to perform these reactions.

Arsenate poisoning: The poison arsenate (AsO_4^{3-}) uncouples the phosphorylation and oxidation by competing with PO_4^{2-} for this -SH site. The resulting arseno-3 phosphoglycerate is not stable and no ATP is made from this reaction. Similar inhibitions with other phosphorylation reactions result from arsenic poisoning.

Step 7. First ATP synthesis by transferring high energy phosphate group from 1,3 BPG to ADP (substrate level phosphorylation). This is the first yield of 2 ATPs from two trioses balancing the first investment of 2 ATPs per glucose.

2 (1, 3- Bisphosphoglycerate) → 2 (3- phosphoglycerate)

Step 8. Transfer of phosphate from 3rd to 2nd C. The phosphate group of 3-phosphoglycerate is transferred from 3rd C to 2nd C to generate 2-phosphoglycerate by phosphoglyceromutase.

Step 9. Removal of H_2O from 2-PGA. A water molecule is removed from 2-PGA by enolase to create a double bond between the 2nd C and 3rd C to make the phosphate bond unstable in the new compound phosphoenolpyruvate (PEP).

2 (2-phosphoglycerate) ——→ 2 H_2O ——→ 2 (Phosphoenolpyruvate)

Step 10. Second ATP synthesis. The phosphate from PEP is transferred to ADP (second substrate level phosphorylation) to generate two more ATPs which is the net ATP synthesis in cytoplasm during glycolysis.

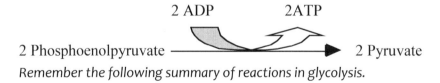

2 Phosphoenolpyruvate ——→ 2 Pyruvate

Remember the following summary of reactions in glycolysis.

Summary of reactions in glycolysis
> Inputs: Glucose + 2 NAD+ + 2 ADP + 2 Pi →
> Outputs: 2 Pyruvate + 2 NADH + 2 H+ + 2 ATP (net)

Electron Shuttles

The 2 pyruvates are transferred into mitochondria by a specific transport protein. The 2 ATPs made are used in cytoplasm. In aerobic respiration, the NADH transfers its electrons to a mitochondrial FAD or NAD$^+$ to be used in the electron transport chain. Since NADH is a large molecule, it cannot enter the mitochondria and this e$^-$ transfer into mitochondria is done by a shuttle mechanism. Two such mechanisms are the glycerol 3-phosphate shuttle and malate-aspartate shuttle. The NAD+ should be regenerated to keep the gly-colysis going. The shuttle helps in the regeneration of NAD+ needed in gly-colysis.

1. Glycerol 3-phosphate shuttle

The NADH from glycolysis transfers the electrons to dihydroxy acetone phosphate (DHAP) to form glycerol 3-phosphate, which diffuses into mi-tochondria wherein the electrons are transferred to mitochondrial FAD to generate $FADH_2$ and dihydroxy acetone phosphate. The dihydroxy acetone phosphate diffuses out to perform the shuttle reaction again. The NAD^+ re-generated in cytoplasm returns to glycolysis to accept another pair of elec-trons.

2. Malate-Aspartate

In heart and liver cells the cytoplasmic NADH transfers electrons to a mi-tochondrial NADH by a different shuttle, namely malate-aspartate shuttle. In this case, the mitochondrial NADH results in 3 ATPs for each NADH from glycolysis. The $FADH_2$ made in the first shuttle mechanism results in only 2 ATPs for each NADH from glycolysis.

III. Acetyl CoA Formation

This step of pyruvate decarboxylation and acetyl CoA formation occurs before Krebs cycle. The pyruvate from glycolysis is transported into mito-chondria. The **pyruvate dehydrogenase** complex on the inner mitochondrial membrane oxidizes pyruvate and converts it into acetyl CoA.

In this process, one CO_2 is released from pyruvate and an NAD^+ is re-duced to NADH. Acetyl CoA is also generated from fats which are broken down to generate energy through Krebs cycle and oxidative phosphoryla-tion. This reaction is irreversible and highly regulated. Pyruvate dehydroge-nase is inhibited by high levels of acetyl CoA, NADH and GTP and induced by high levels of CoA, NAD^+ and GDP.

Pyruvate dehydrogenase is a complex protein with three enzymes combined together and uses thiamine pyrophosphate (TPP), FAD and li-poamide as cofactors. **Beri beri** is a neurological and cardiovascular disorder caused by a lack of thiamine (vitamin B1).

Acetyl CoA is also formed from the **beta-oxidation of lipids** and from the proteins after hydrolysis and deamination. Thus acetyl CoA is a common intermediate that can be obtained from carbohydrates, lipids and proteins. This step of acetyl CoA formation is not part of the Krebs cycle.

It is interesting to note the conversion of excess carbohydrates into stored fat involves the intermediate of acetylCoA. The excess acetyl CoA which can not be used in Krebs cycle is converted to malonyl CoA and other intermediates and is stored as fat.

Summary of acetyl CoA formation from pyruvate oxidation
Inputs: Pyruvate + NAD^+ + CoA
Outputs: Acetyl CoA + NADH

IV. Krebs Cycle

The Krebs cycle was named after Hans Krebs who elucidated most of the pathway. This is also called the **tricarboxylic acid (TCA) cycle** or **citric acid cycle**. This process occurs mainly in the matrix and on the inner membrane of mitochondria.

Step 1. This is the first committed step performed by citrate synthase which is induced by AMP and inhibited by ATP.

$$Acetyl\ CoA\ (2\ C) + Oxaloacetate\ (4\ C) \xrightarrow{H_2O} Citrate\ (6\ C) + CoA + H^+$$

Step 2. This isomerization is done through dehydration and hydration of citrate through an intermediate cis-aconitate by aconitase.

$$Citrate\ (6\text{-}C) \underset{aconitase}{\overset{}{\rightleftarrows}} Isocitrate\ (6\text{-}C)$$

Step 3. Oxidative decarboxylation of isocitrate by isocitrate dehydrogenase is the rate limiting step (controls the reaction rate of Krebs cycle). Isocitrate dehydrogenase is stimulated by ADP which enhances its affinity for its substrates isocitrate and NAD^+. The enzyme is inhibited by high levels of NADH and ATP.

$$Isocitrate\ (6\text{-}C) \xrightarrow[]{NAD^+ + H^+ \quad \rightarrow \quad NADH + CO_2 + H^+} a\text{-}ketoglutarate\ (5\text{-}C)$$

Step 4. This is the third level of control in the Krebs cycle. NADH, succinyl CoA and ATP inhibit the activity of α-ketoglutarate dehydrogenase. So far two CO_2 molecules have been released in the Krebs cycle from the 6-C compound citrate resulting in the 4-C compound succinate which will be gradually converted into oxaloacetate in the following steps (5 to 8) to continue the cycle.

$$a\text{-}ketoglutarate + CoA \xrightarrow[a\text{-}ketoglutarate\ dehydrogenase]{NAD^+ \quad \rightarrow \quad NADH + CO_2} Succinyl\ CoA\ (4\text{-}C)$$

Step 5. This reaction results in the substrate-level phosphorylation of ADP to generate an ATP by transferring the phosphate from GTP to ADP. The P_i (pyrophosphate) is obtained from the matrix.

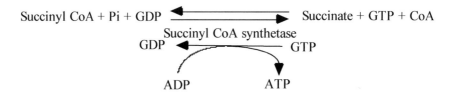

Succinyl CoA + Pi + GDP $\rightleftharpoons$ Succinate + GTP + CoA

Succinyl CoA synthetase

GDP $\leftarrow$ — GTP

ADP   ATP

Step 6. This is another set of electrons being transferred to FAD for later use in oxidative phosphorylation.

Succinate + FAD $\rightleftharpoons$ Fumarate + $FADH_2$

Succinate
dehydragenase

Step 7. This a preparation to extract more electrons to reduce NAD^+.

Fumarate $\frac{+}{2}$ $\rightleftharpoons$ Malate

Fumarase

Step 8. This is the last NADH made in Krebs cycle. So far 2 NADH, 1 ATP and 1 FADH2 have been made from each acetyl CoA that enters Krebs cycle.

Malate + NAD^+ $\rightleftharpoons$ Oxaloacetate + NADH

Malate dehydrogenase

Since there are two pyruvates from each glucose resulting in two acetyl CoAs, the Kreb's cycle occurs twice for each glucose.

Summary of Krebs cycle reactions

Inputs: Acetyl CoA + 3 NAD+ + FAD + ADP + P_i + $2H_2O$

Outputs: $2 CO_2$ + 3 NADH + 3H+ + $FADH_2$ + ATP + CoA

V. Oxidative Phosphorylation

Oxidation refers to the loss of electrons from NADH and $FADH_2$ to a series of membrane proteins called as **electron transport chain** (ETC). The ETC finally transfer the electrons to oxygen, the final electron acceptor, to generate water (along with 2 H^+).

During this process of electron transfer, protons are pumped out of the matrix into the intermembrane space, making it acidic (forming a proton gradient). As the protons return to the matrix through ATP synthase (proton motive force), they help in the formation and release of ATP from the enzyme. This whole process is referred to as oxidative phosphorylation.

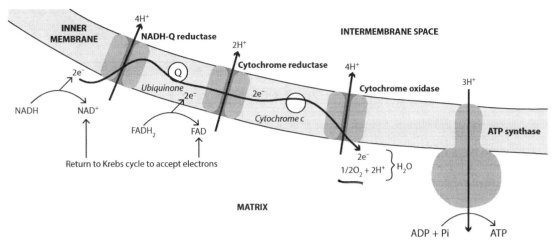

Figure 9-7.   **Oxidative phosphorylation**

Transfer of electrons from NADH and FADH$_2$ to electron transport chain

NADH transfers the electrons to NADH-Q reductase and gets reduced to NAD$^+$, which returns to the mitochondrial NAD$^+$ pool to accept electrons from the Krebs cycle. FADH$_2$ transfers electrons at a lower energy level to ubiquinone (Coenzyme Q-10 or CoQ), a mobile electron carrier. FADH$_2$ then becomes FAD and returns to the Krebs cycle. The Krebs cycle cannot continue without having enough NAD$_+$ and FAD for the oxidation of acetyl CoA.

Since FADH$_2$ delivers electrons at the lower energy level, fewer ATPs are made from its electron transfer as explained below. The electrons from NADH and FADH$_2$ are transferred through cytochrome reductase and cytochrome oxidase and finally are accepted by oxygen (molecular oxygen is used here). Oxygen is the ultimate electron acceptor in aerobic respiration. The two electrons, two protons (from the matrix) and oxygen from O$_2$ generates water in matrix. It is interesting to note that CO$_2$ is released from the decarboxylation of pyruvate and from the Krebs cycle long before O$_2$ is consumed in oxidative phosphorylation.

Generation of [H+] gradient and ATP synthesis

When electrons are transferred through the membrane proteins they generate an electrical imbalance resulting in the transfer of protons from the matrix into the intermembrane space. The specific details are not well known.

For each pair of electrons, approximately two to four protons are transported into the intermembrane space. When approximately three protons return from the intermembrane space into matrix through the ATP synthase, this proton motive force helps to release ATP which is made by and tightly bound to the enzyme. Another proton is used to transport the ATP from the matrix to the cytoplasm through a membrane protein ATP/ADP-translocase. So approximately three to four protons are needed to make and transport one ATP. Since the oxidation of NADH and FADH$_2$ results in the transport of approximately 10 and 6 protons respectively, they result in making three and two ATPs each respectively.

Summary of Oxidative Phosphorylation

Inputs: NADH, FADH2, ADP, Pi, O2
Outputs: NAD$^+$, FAD, ATP and H2O

Summary of ATP synthesis in aerobic respiration

Process	ATP made per Glucose	ATP made per Acetyl-CoA
Glycolysis	2	0
Krebs cycle	2	1
Oxidative Phosphorylation	32-34	11

Summary of NADH/FADH2 synthesis in aerobic respiration

Process	NADH made per Glucose	FADH$_2$ per Glucose	NADH per Acetyl-CoA	FADH$_2$ per Acetyl-CoA
Glycolysis	2	0	0	0
Acetyl CoA Formation	2	0	0	0
Krebs cycle	6	2	3	1

Respiratory poisons

The three classes of respiratory poisons, their mechanism of action and the examples are as follows:

1. Uncouplers of proton gradient: abolish proton gradient by making the membrane leaky, resulting in no ATP synthesis, e.g: dinitrophenol (DNP)
2. ATP synthase inhibitors: directly bind to ATP synthase and inhibit ATP synthesis, e.g.: oligomycin
3. Electron transport inhibitors: block electron transport at various stages, resulting in reduced or lack of proton gradient and ATP synthesis; mainly block O_2 from accepting electrons, stopping the regeneration of NAD^+ and FAD (without which Krebs cycle cannot function), e.g.: Cyanide (CN-), carbon monoxide (CO) and azide (N3-) bind to cytochrome oxidase and block electron transfer to O_2. *It is not critical to memorize these poisons.*

VI. Anaerobic Respiration and Fermentation

A. Anaerobic respiration

Anaerobic respiration is complete respiration without O_2; NO_3^- or SO_4^- accepts the electrons from the electron transport chain instead. All the other reactions go on in a similar manner. This process is limited to facultative anaerobes that can live under a NO_3^- or SO_4^- rich environment.

B. Anaerobic fermentation

No oxygen nor any other molecule is available to receive electrons from the electron transport chain. ATPs are made through glycolysis only. NAD^+ needs to be regenerated to keep the glycolysis going, either through alcoholic fermentation or lactic acid fermentation as explained below.

1. Alcohol Fermentation

The two pyruvates made from glucose during glycolysis are decarboxylated by pyruvate decarboxylase to generate acetaldehyde. The CO_2 released during this decarboxylation is what makes bread rise and beer froth. The acetaldehyde is hydrogenated to form ethanol, using NADH as the reducing agent by alcohol dehydrogenase, thus regenerating the NAD$^+$ needed for glycolysis to continue. Alcohol is a byproduct in alcoholic fermentation.

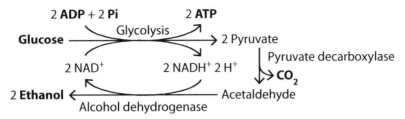

Figure 9-8. Alcohol fermentation

Summary of alcohol fermentation
        Inputs: glucose + 2 ADP + 2Pi
        Outputs: 2 Ethanol + 2 CO$_2$ + 2 ATP

2. Lactic acid fermentation

Animals do not have pyruvate decarboxylase, so they perform lactic acid fermentation in muscle cells to regenerate NAD$^+$ during O$_2$ deprivation. In muscle cells, NAD$^+$ is regenerated by converting the pyruvate into lactate which returns to the liver to be reconverted into glucose for later use. This lactic acid accumulation and micro tears cause muscle fatigue during strenuous exercise with limited O$_2$ levels. Lactate fermentation is an important contributor for quick burst of energy under emergency situations.

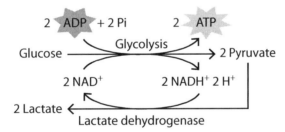

Figure 9-9. Lactate fermentation

Summary of lactate fermentation
        Inputs: glucose + 2 ADP + 2Pi
        Outputs: 2 lactate + 2 ATP

Pasteur Effect: Louis Pasteur observed that yeast growing under anaerobic conditions consumed more sugar than yeast grown under aerobic conditions. This is called the Pasteur effect and can be explained by the fact that yeast generates less ATP (two/glucose) under anaerobic conditions than under aerobic conditions (30 - 32 ATPs/glucose). So, to maintain the same growth rate, anaerobic yeast consumes a lot more sugar, up to 100 times more than aerobic yeast.

10. PHOTOSYNTHESIS

Concepts

- The ultimate source of energy for almost all living systems is the sun.
- Plants and other photosynthetic organisms have special structures and molecules to harness the sun's energy.
- A series of reactions occur in photosynthetic cells to harvest light energy in the form of ATP and NADPH.
- The chemical energy in the form of ATP and NADPH are used to fix CO_2 in the form of carbohydrates for energy or storage and making other organic molecules.

Outline

I. Basic Concepts
   (Leaf anatomy, basic reactions, light energy and pigments)
II. Light Dependent Reactions
   (Photosystems, cyclic photophosphorylation, non-cyclic photophosphorylation)
III. Calvin Cycle
   (Carbon fixation, reduction, regeneration of RuBP, photorespiration)
IV. Variations of Calvin Cycle
   (C3, C4, CAM pathways)

The ultimate source of energy for this living planet comes from the sun. Photosynthetic algae, bacteria and plants can utilize the solar energy to fix atmospheric CO_2 into carbohydrates. Photosynthesis generates carbohydrates and other organic compounds from which all other organic molecules are made. This chapter covers the structure of the photosynthetic apparatus; how light energy is transformed into chemical energy; how CO_2 is fixed into organic molecules; and some of the variations within photosynthesis. We will focus mainly on photosynthesis in plants.

1. Basic Concepts

Based on how an organism obtains its food, we can classify them into the following categories. **Autotrophic organisms** make their own food by biochemical processes. They generate carbon compounds and their own food from chemicals from surroundings (**chemoautotrophic**, e.g.: bacteria) or through photosynthesis (**photoautotrophic**, e.g.: plants). **Heterotrophic organisms** survive by feeding on other organisms. Animals, fungi and many bacteria are heterotrophs. They depend on photoautotrophs for food and also oxygen that is released during photosynthesis.

A. Leaf anatomy:

Leaves are designed to harvest light energy with their chloroplasts located in photosynthetic cells. A cross section of a leaf is shown below. Photosynthesis generally occurs in mesophyll cells containing abundant chloroplasts.

There are approximately 50 million chloroplasts per cm² in an actively growing green leaf. Light reactions (converting light energy into chemical energy -NADPH) occur on the thylakoid membranes, and the protons are pumped from the stroma into the thylakoid space. When they return to the stroma, protons help ATP synthesis (photophosphorylation). The ATPs and NADPH are used to fix CO_2. CO_2 enters the leaf through stomatal pores and is converted to carbohydrates in the stroma. The carbohydrates made in the stroma are transported into large veins via smaller veins; both large and small veins contain phloem to transport sugars to other parts of the plant for use or storage. Xylem elements in veins help transport water and minerals.

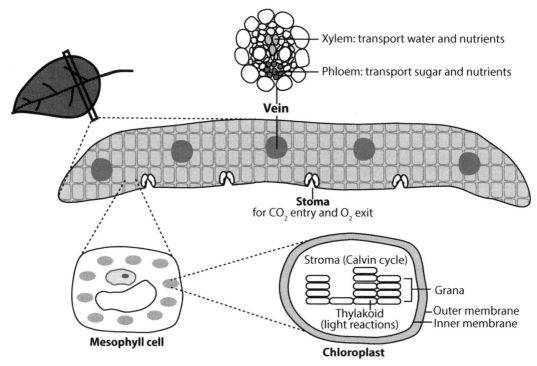

Figure 10-1. Leaf anatomy

B. Basic reactions:

In photosynthesis the overall set of reactions may be summarized as follows:

$$6CO_2 + 12 H_2O \longrightarrow C_6H_{12}O_6 + 6O_2 + 6 H_2O$$

Using radioactive oxygen (^{18}O), research has shown that the O_2 evolved (released) from the photosynthesis reaction comes from the splitting of a water molecule. The release of O_2 occurs during the light reactions to replenish the two electrons lost from photosystem II (see details later). CO_2 is fixed into carbohydrates during dark (i.e.: light-independent) reactions.

Photosynthesis is also a redox process involving $NADP^+$ (nicotinamide adenine dinucleotide phosphate) as the electron carrier. $NADP^+$ receives electrons from the light reactions and transfers them to the Calvin cycle to generate carbohydrates.

Photophosphorylation

Electron transfer through a series of thylakoid membrane proteins results in the generation of a proton gradient inside the thylakoid, which becomes acidic. When protons return to the stroma through ATP synthase, they help in the synthesis of ATP, as in the chemiosmosis of respiration.

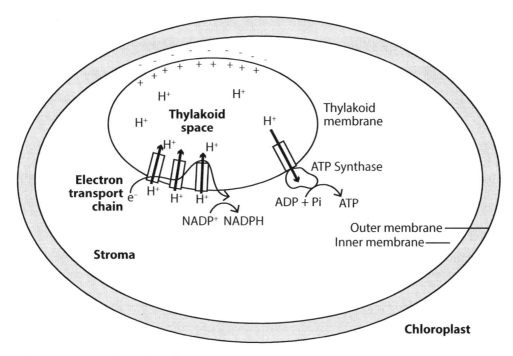

Figure 10-2.   **Photophosphorylation**

C. Light energy and pigments

Sunlight is a form of electromagnetic wave energy with particulate photons. It is emitted from fusion reactions occurring in the sun. The energy of photons is inversely proportional to their wavelengths (distance between the two crests of electromagnetic waves). The wavelengths of the visible light range from 380 nm to 750 nm and consist of red, orange, yellow, green, blue, indigo and violet (ROY-G-BIV). Green is the least effective because most of it is reflected or transmitted (that is why most plants look green). Blue and red are the most effective because chlorophyll and other pigments absorb maximum light in these wavelength ranges.

Photosystems are light-harvesting complexes with the following components:

1. Chlorophyll a, b and other pigments to absorb light.
2. A reaction center: specialized chlorophyll a molecules to emit excited electrons.
3. The primary electron acceptor.

Leaves contain photosynthetic pigments such as chlorophyll a, chlorophyll b, β-carotene and phycocyanin. These pigments contain a porphyrin ring with Mg^{2+} in the middle and a long hydrocarbon chain, which anchors them on the thylakoid membrane. These pigments absorb light at a specific wavelength range (shown by the absorption spectrum) with a defined peak (the maximum absorption). Photons are absorbed by these pigments and converted into chemical energy within a range of wavelengths (shown by action spectrum), which may be different from the absorption spectrum.

Photosynthetic pigments are located around reaction centers containing two chlorophyll a molecules. When various pigments receive photons of a specific wavelength, they pass that energy to reaction center chlorophyll. A pair of electrons in the reaction center chlorophyll is excited to a higher energy level, proportional to the energy level of the photons received. The excited electrons are absorbed by primary electron acceptor proteins and go through a series of membrane proteins comprising the electron transport chain, resulting in ATP and NADPH synthesis.

11. Light Reactions

Photosystems

The light reactions (light-dependent reactions) occur on the thylakoid membrane, containing photosystems I and II, which harvest light energy to generate ATP and NADPH in the stroma.

There are two types of photosystems as shown below.

Photosystem I (PS I)	Photosystem II (PS II)
Reaction center chlorophyll a absorbs light with 700 nm peak	Reaction center chlorophyll a absorbs light with 680 nm peak
Reduce $NADP^+$ to NADPH in non-cyclic photophosphorylation	Split water into two H^+, 2 e^- and 1/2 O_2
ATP synthesis	ATP synthesis
Present in both cyclic and non-cyclic photophosphorylation	Functions in only non-cyclic photophosphorylation
Primitive in evolution	More recent in evolution

The excited electrons are transferred in two different ways in cyclic and non-cyclic photophosphorylation with different results.

Cyclic photophosphorylation

The excited electrons from the PS I reaction center are received by the primary electron acceptor and transferred to ferredoxin (Fd; a protein), plastoquinone (PQ; an organic molecule), cytochrome (Cyt; a protein complex), plastocyanin (PC; a reducing agent) and finally back to the photosystem I reaction center. The electron transport is utilized to create a proton gradient to drive ATP synthesis.

During cyclic photophosphorylation, water is not split, oxygen is not evolved and NADPH is not made. This process occurs in primitive plants and when no NADPH is needed (i.e.: in a high NADPH/$NADP^+$ ratio environment).

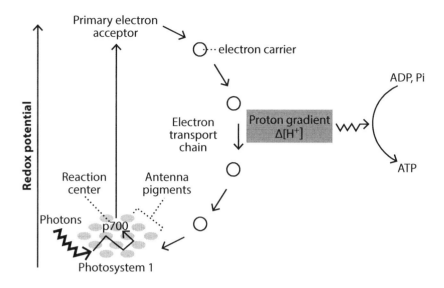

Figure 10-3. **Cyclic Electron Transfer**

Non-cyclic photophosphorylation

In non-cyclic photophosphorylation both PS I and PS II are involved. The electrons do not return to the starting place (reaction center) and end up in NADPH. The electrons lost by PS II after receiving photons are replaced by extracting electrons from the splitting of water. The excited electrons from the PS II reaction center are accepted by the primary electron acceptor, transferred to pheophytin (Ph or I; an oxidizing agent), plastoquinone, the cytochrome complex and plastocyanin and finally to the PS I reaction center which had earlier lost excited electrons to its primary electron acceptor.

The electrons lost by PS II are replaced by the splitting of water molecules into oxygen, protons and electrons. O_2 is released from PS II long before CO_2 is fixed into sugars. Oxygen-releasing plants evolved later and made our atmosphere rich in O_2 and suitable for other aerobic organisms. The electrons from PS I are transferred to a membrane-bound ferredoxin, a soluble ferredoxin and finally are used to reduce $NADP^+$ to generate NADPH. ATP is generated during the electron transfer from PS II to PS I.

The products of light reactions such as ATP and NADPH, generated in the stroma, are used in the Calvin cycle (see the table below) to fix CO_2 into carbohydrates. ATP is hydrolyzed into ADP; and NADPH is oxidized to $NADP^+$ during the Calvin cycle. These return to the light reactions to be converted again into ATP and NADPH, respectively.

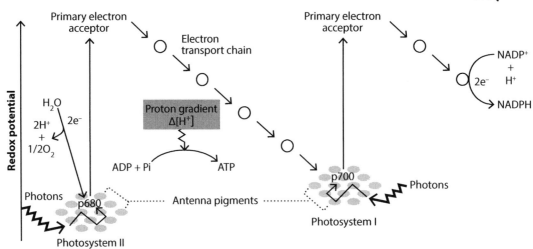

Figure 10-4.   **Non-Cyclic Electron Transfer**

Cyclic Electron Transfer	Non-cyclic Electron Transfer
Primitive (involves only PS I)	Evolved later (uses both PS I and II)
Electrons return to PS I reaction center	Electrons do not return to reaction center
ATP synthesized in PS I	ATP synthesized in PS II
No NADPH made	Electrons used to generate NADPH
No O_2 is evolved	O_2 is evolved from the splitting of water
Electron recylced	H_2O is the ultimate electron source
Occurs when NADPH level is high	Most common in plants

III. Calvin Cycle

These reactions are light-independent, i.e. can occur in dark or light. However, they need the ATP and NADPH produced in the light reactions. These reactions are called the Calvin-Benson cycle or simply Calvin cycle, named after its discoverers, Melvin Calvin and Andrew Benson. It is also called C3 cycle because CO_2 is first fixed into a 3-C compound. The three major stages of Calvin cycle are carbon fixation, reduction and regeneration of RuBP. The steps involved in the cycle are summarized below.

Carbon fixation reactions

Step 1. CO_2 is combined with a 5-C compound ribulose bisphosphate (RuBP) to generate two 3-C compounds 3-phosphoglycerate by the enzyme ribulose bisphosphate carboxylase/oxygenase (rubisco).

$$3\ CO_2 + 3\ (\text{ribulose bispphosphate}) \xrightarrow{\text{Rubisco}} 6\ (\text{3-phosphoglycerate})$$

This is a key regulatory step of the C3 cycle controlling the synthesis of sugars by CO_2 fixation. This regulation is explained later in the chapter.

Reduction reactions

Step 2. Phosphorylation of 3-phosphoglycerate into 1,3-bisphospho-glycerate by phosphoglycerate kinase. This is the first step in the C3 cycle to use ATPs generated in the light reaction.

Step 3. 1,3-bisphosphoglycerate is dephosphorylated and reduced to glyceraldehyde 3-phosphate. The high energy 1-phosphate and the reducing power of NADPH obtained from the light reactions are used here.

$$6\ NADPH \qquad\qquad 6\ NADP^+ + 6\ Pi$$

6 (1,3-bisphosphoglycerate) $\longrightarrow$ 6 (Glyceraldehyde 3-phosphate)

Glyceraldehyde 3-phosphate dehydrogenase.

Step 4. Glucose and other carbohydrates are synthesized from 1 out of 6 molecules of glyceraldehyde 3-phosphate through several steps. You need two sets of reactions described above to generate one hexose. These steps resemble the reverse of glycolysis to generate 6-C sugars from 3-C sugars.

(Glyceraldehyde 3-phosphate) $\longrightarrow \longrightarrow$ glucose + other sugars.

Sucrose and starch are the major forms of storage carbohydrates in plants.

Regeneration of RuBP

Step 5. Regeneration of ribulose bisphophate to continue the cycle. Five glyceraldehyde 3-phosphates (3-C) are used in a series of steps to regenerate 3 molecules of ribulose bisphosphate (5-C). This goes to step 1 to fix another 3 CO_2 molecules to generate 6 3-C sugars. Some more ATPs are used in these steps to generate RuBP.

$$3\ ATP \qquad\qquad 3\ ADP$$

5 (glyceraldehyde 3-phosphate) $\longrightarrow$ 3 (ribulose bisphosphate)

Summary of Calvin cycle and Light Reactions
With two sets of reactions shown above, we can summarize the results of the light reactions and C3 cycle as follows.

Inputs: 6 CO_2 + 18 ATP + 12 NADPH + 12 H_2O →
Outputs: $C_6H_{12}O_6$ + 18 ADP + 18 P_i + 12 $NADP^+$ + 6 H_2O + 12 H^+ + 6 O_2

Thus to generate one molecule of hexose such as glucose or fructose, 18 molecules of ATP and 12 molecules of NADPH are needed (3 ATPs and 2 NADPH per CO_2).

Regulation of Rubisco
Rubisco (RuBP carboxylase and oxygenase) is probably the most abundant protein on earth; up to 50% of a leaf's soluble protein is rubisco. It comprises 8 large subunits of 55 kDa each and 8 small subunits of 15 kDa, each making the whole enzyme complex approximately 560 kDa in size. The large subunit is the catalytic subunit and is made in the chloroplast. The small subunit is the regulatory subunit, generated in the cytoplasm and imported

into the chloroplast. Rubisco can fix both CO_2 (carboxylase) and O_2 (oxygenase) into RuBP. Fixing O_2 into RuBP is called **photorespiration** which will be explained later.

Rubisco is regulated by the following factors:

1. *Concentration of CO_2 and O_2 in the cell*: Since rubisco can fix both CO_2 and O_2, it is sensitive to their concentrations. When the level of CO_2 decreases after the Calvin cycle, rubisco starts to fix oxygen and release CO_2 during photorespiration.
2. *Mg^{2+} concentration*: Rubisco activity requires Mg^{2+}. The level of Mg^{2+} increases in the stroma upon illumination to facilitate carbon fixation.
3. *pH*: When light reactions are in operation, the pH in the stroma increases from 7 to 8 which is the optimal pH of rubisco.
4. *NADPH levels*: The activity of rubisco is stimulated by greater levels of NADPH generated during light reactions.

Photorespiration

On hot, sunny and dry days, when the stomatal pores in leaves are closed to conserve moisture, the CO_2 intensity falls to a low level, concomitant with the rise of O_2; in this case, rubisco utilizes the process of photorespiration to fix O_2 into RuBP in a series of reactions that finally releases CO_2. This results in the use of RuBP without making any sugars or ATP. This process occurs until the CO_2 levels are back to normal within the cell.

IV. Variations of the Calvin Cycle

A. C3 plants

- Only Calvin cycle is used to fix CO_2.
- The C3 pathway evolved earlier than C4 or CAM pathways.
- The majority of plants are C3 (e.g: rice, wheat).

B. C4 plants

Plants have developed alternative strategies to overcome photorespiration and maximize CO_2 fixation using the *C4 pathway*. This pathway involves an enzyme called phosphoenolpyruvate carboxylase (PEP carboxylase) which fixes CO_2 into 4-C sugars (hence the name). PEP carboxylase has no affinity for O_2, so even when CO_2 levels decrease during hot sunny weather, CO_2 fixation continues and photorespiration is minimized.

- C4 plants use both C3 and C4 pathways to fix CO_2.
- The C3 pathway is limited to bundle sheath cells (adjacent to veins); the C4 pathway is limited to mesophyll cells (closer to the surface).
- C4 plants are efficient in CO_2 fixation and using water effectively (e.g.: corn, sugarcane).

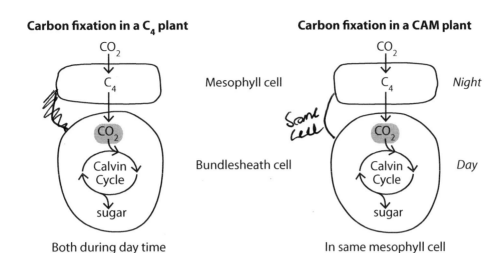

Carbon fixation in a C₄ plant

CO₂
C₄
CO₂
Calvin Cycle
sugar

Both during day time

Mesophyll cell

Bundlesheath cell

Carbon fixation in a CAM plant

CO₂
C₄   Night
CO₂
Calvin Cycle   Day
sugar

Scent cell

In same mesophyll cell

Figure 10-5.   **Carbon fixation in C4 and CAM plants**

C. CAM plants

Crassulacean Acid Metabolism was first discovered in the family Crassula-ceae. These plants also operate both C3 and C4 cycles to fix CO_2 into 4-C sugars first and thereafter into 3-C sugars.

- CAM plants do not have separate cells for C3 and C4 pathways.
- CAM plants carry out C3 reactions during the day (stomata are closed due to hot sunny weather and ATP and NADPH are available).
- Use C4 reactions during nighttime (stomata are open in cooler weather and CO_2 is available).

- Many succulent desert plants use this strategy to fix CO_2 (e.g. cacti).

Photosynthesis involves light reactions to generate ATP and NADPH which are used in the Calvin cycle to fix CO_2 into 3-carbon (C3 plant) or 4-carbon (C4 and CAM plants) sugars, which eventually become hexose and polysac-charides.

Carbohydrates are the major source of energy and provide carbon-skeletons to generate other organic products. During light reactions, O_2 is evolved, enriching the atmosphere with O_2 for respiration. Thus, photosyn-thesis is vital for the existence of almost all the living organisms in the world by providing the primary source of food to eat and the oxygen to breath.

FLOW OF GENETIC INFORMATION

Genetic information flows from DNA to RNA to protein, and can be inherited from cell to cell as well as from generation to generation.

Chapters

11. CELL DIVISION - MITOSIS

Concepts

- Cell division is essential for reproduction, repair, growth and development.
- Bacterial cells divide by a simple process called binary fission.
- Eukarytic somatic cells undergo a cell cycle that includes mitosis as the cell division process.
- Cell cycle stages and reproduction are tightly regulated by proteins and environmental conditions.

Outline

I.   Bacterial reproduction (binary fission)
II. Mitosis (somatic cell division)
III. Regulation of cell division

Cell division is a very important process in every organism to replicate life, grow and develop, repair damaged organs and protect living cells. Prokaryotes, unicellular and multicellular eukaryotes, such as plants and animals, divide and undergo cell division in their own unique ways. The common aspects in all cell divisions are DNA replication and division of other parts of the cell in an approximately equal manner. The cell division processes in bacteria, animals and plants are explained in this chapter.

1. Bacterial Reproduction

Prokaryotes (bacteria and archaebacteria) divide by **binary fission**. The basic genetic elements of a bacterial cell, shown below, include the following:

A. Plasmid DNA
   - extra chromosomal circular DNA molecules
   - contain an origin of replication (a specific region of DNA recognized by DNA replication enzymes) and genes coding for antibiotic resistance or enzymes to make specific nutrients
   - vary in size (ranging from 3 to 140 kbp) and in the number of genes they carry
   - replicate independent of the chromosomal DNA
   Types of plasmids:
   - R-plasmids: These are the plasmids containing antibiotic resistance genes. These are the genes that allow some disease causing bacteria to develop resistance against commonly used antibiotics.
   - F-plasmids: These are fertility plasmids which contain genes for making F-pili (reproductive part to transmit DNA during bacterial mating). F-plasmids are transmitted through sexual mating.
   - C-factors: Colicinogenic factors contain genes coding for toxins, important for the survival of the bacteria.

B. Chromosomal DNA
- large (~ 5,000 kbp) and circular
- contains a single origin of replication and is bound to the plasma membrane; not bound by a protein envelope
- confined to a region called the nucleoid region
- replicates once per cell division while attached to the plasma membrane (plasmids replicate independent of bacterial cell division)

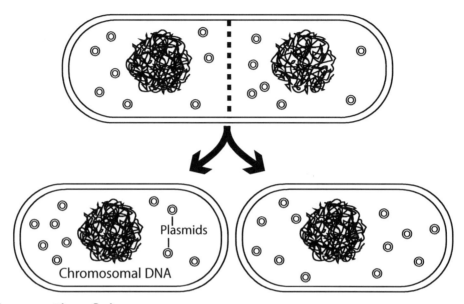

Figure 11-1. Binary fission

Once a bacterium replicates its chromosomal DNA with a sufficient number of plasmid DNA and other cell contents, the plasma membrane grows inward to divide the cell in two. A new cell wall is formed between the two daughter cells. Each of the daughter cells has one copy of chromosomal DNA, a random number of plasmid DNA and other components of the cell. This process is called binary fission. Bacteria such as *Escherichia coli* divide approximately once every 20 minutes.

11. Mitosis

Mitosis is the process by which eukaryotic cells replicate their DNA into two identical copies and divide to form two identical cells. All somatic and vegetative cells divide by mitosis. Identical twins and clones are also produced by mitosis.

A. Genetic elements of eukaryotic cells

Eukaryotic cells have linear **chromosomes**, which are organized into **chromatin** (DNA + protein loosely dispersed in the nucleus) in actively growing cells. The chromosomal DNA is bound to **histones**, group of proteins that DNA winds around to form **nucleosomes** (small beads of DNA and histones). Condensed nucleosomes form the looped domains of chromatin, which condense to form chromosomes during the metaphase stage of cell division. Chromatin is made up of approximately 35% DNA, 60% proteins and 5% RNA. **Genes** are defined by specific DNA sequences in the chromosomes and may encode different kinds of RNA and a large variety of proteins.

Once a chromosome is replicated, making two identical copies, the two strands, called **sister chromatids**, are attached at the center. (It is still considered a single chromosome.) The central region of the attachment is called the **centromere** and the ends are called **telomeres**. Since eukaryotic chromosomes are large, they may have multiple origins of replication at which the DNA replicating enzymes bind to initiate the DNA replication.

All somatic cells of a species have the same number of chromosomes. The number is unique to that particular species. Reproductive cells (**gametes**) contain half that number. Higher eukaryotes do not have plasmids but some fungi may contain plasmids. Organelles such as chloroplasts and mitochondria contain their own chromosomes, similar to prokaryotic chromosomes (circular DNA); these organelles replicate on their own by binary fission.

B. Cell cycle

The cell cycle consists of two major phases, namely, *interphase* and *mitotic (M) phase*. Interphase is divided into G_1, S and G_2 phases. Mitotic phase is divided into *prophase, prometaphase, metaphase, anaphase* and finally *telophase and cytokinesis*.

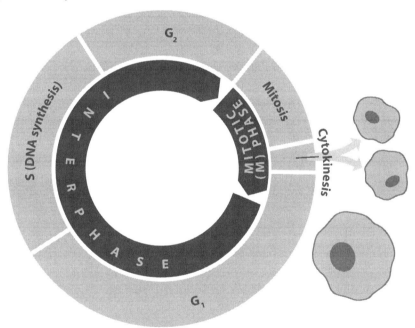

Figure 11-2. Cell cycle

1. Interphase
G_1 (Gap 1): rapid growth and metabolic activity
Centrioles, made up of microtubules, replicate in the middle of microtubule organizing centers (MTOC) with microtubules radiating from the center.
S-phase (DNA Synthesis): replication
Chromosomes replicate along with their proteins but are still loosely dispersed as chromatin. The replicated DNA is identical to the parental chromosome. The individual strands of chromosomes are called sister chromatids which remain attached at the centromere region.

G$_2$ (Gap 2): growth and final preparation
All organelles and membranes are duplicated throughout interphase. Chloroplasts and mitochondria also have replicated by binary fission.

2. M-phase (Mitosis + cytokinesis)
Mitosis occurs in 4 distinct phases.
Prophase: sometimes divided into prophase and prometaphase
Prophase: preparation for cell division occurs
The nucleolus disappears, the chromatin gets denser and forms chromatids. The two pairs of centrioles (*asters*) move to opposite poles. In the cytoplasm, the mitotic spindle (made up of microtubules) forms from the MTOC (in plants) or centrioles (in animals).
Prometaphase: the nuclear envelope fragments and disappears
Microtubules of spindle fibers (polar fibers) are connected to the chromosomes at places called the *kinetochore* (15-35 microtubules per kinetochore). The fibers attached here are called kinetochore fibers and others are called non-kinetochore fibers.
Metaphase: the final preparation before the chromatids seperate
The sister chromatids of replicated chromosomes are aligned in the middle of the cell at the *metaphase plate.*
Anaphase: the centromere of each chromosome divides
Each newly formed chromosome moves apart to separate the sister chromatids into two single-stranded chromosomes. Chromosomes move approximately 1 µm/sec due to depolymerization of microtubules near the kinetochore to bring the chromosomes closer to poles. No ATP is needed for this process.
Telophase: two nuclei form to separate sister chromosomes
Polar fibers elongate by adding more microtubules (polymerization) using ATP to expand the cell. Two new nuclei form to envelope the two new groups of daughter chromosomes. Nucleoli reappear inside each nucleus. The chromosomes loosen to become chromatin again.
Cytokinesis: cell splits into two
The cytoplasm furrows inward in the case of animal cells making a *cleavage furrow.* In the case of the plant cell, a *cell plate* forms to divide the two daughter cells, each with its nucleus, chromosomes, organelles etc. The resulting cells are identical in DNA content and number of chromosomes.

All the cells in the body other than reproductive cells divide through mitosis. After cytokinesis, the cells will enter into interphase again to grow and develop or divide again.

Many organisms that reproduce vegetatively use mitosis to divide and differentiate. The possibility of cloning animals from an embryonic cell or totipotent somatic cell is possible because of mitosis resulting in identical progeny. Identical twins are formed naturally due to the mitotic division of the zygote after fertilization. After this mitotic division, the two identical cells continue to divide and develop as separate fetuses. Cell division in somatic cells is a tightly controlled process as explained later in this chapter.

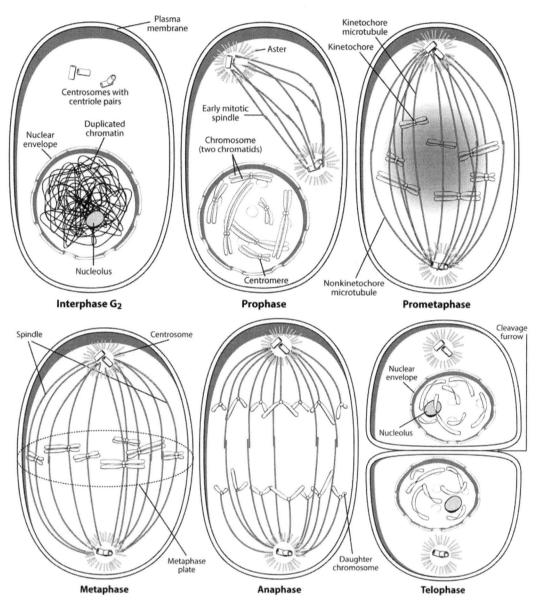

Figure 11-3. Mitosis

III. Regulation of Cell Division

Cell division is a tightly controlled process in the cell, vital to renewing cells, developing new tissues or creating a whole new organism. Proteins and the genes coding for such proteins control checkpoints, growth rate and sequence. Nutritional status, growth factors, hormones, cell density and other environmental factors also influence cell division.

Control of cell division is studied through cell cultures growing in specialized medium, e.g.: plant cell cultures such as maize and tobacco cell suspensions. In human cells, cell lines are sometimes obtained from cancer cells (immortalized cells). These animal cells are grown on monolayer or in suspensions to conduct experiments. The critical stage (restriction point) to control cell division is in the G_1 phase from which the cells go to G_0 (no more division as in nerve cells or muscle cells) or S-phase (synthetic), the G_2 phase and the M phase. Cells divide based on the cytoplasmic volume to DNA ratio.

Proteins regulate the main process of cell division. One such protein is maturation promoting factor (MPF). MPF is a combination of cdk (cyclin dependent kinase) and cyclin that promotes DNA synthesis and mitosis. There are two types of cyclins: S-cyclin, which promotes S-phase, and M-cyclin which promotes M-phase. Depending on the level of cyclin concentration, it binds to cdk. The binding of cyclin to cdc-2 stimulates autophosphorylation of cdk (kinase) and phosphorylation of several other proteins involved in cell division. Some of those proteins are proteases, which can degrade cyclin to bring the levels down to regulate the cycle. So, depending on the phosphorylation status of S-MPF and M-MPF, DNA synthesis or mitosis occurs.

Cell division is an essential process for the replication and survival of life. The bacterial division is through a simple binary fission. Eukaryotic cells go through a relatively complex division cycle called mitosis. The mitotic cycle ensures the production of two daughter cells with the same number and more importantly identical copies of chromosomes. Control of cell division is very critical and several proteins are involved in that process. If the cell division goes out of control, it results in tumors that may be benign or malignant. There are several types of cancers and several ways to detect and treat cancers. The cell cycle is a major and fundamental process of life and while we have come a long way to understand this process, we still have much to learn.

12. MEIOSIS

Concepts

- Sexual reproduction needs two gametes, each of which contains half the number of chromosomes so that when two gametes fertilize, the original chromosome number is regained and maintained in the resulting organism.
- Meiosis occurs only to make reproductive cells or gametes in the male and female reproductive organs.
- Meiosis involves two cell divisions but only one DNA replication.
- Meiosis and random fertilization result in genetic variation among sexually reproduced organisms.

Outline

I. Overview of Sexual Reproduction
II. Meiotic Cell Division
III. Causes of Genetic Variation in Sexual Reproduction

1. Overview of Sexual Reproduction

Meiosis occurs in sex cells to generate reproductive cells (gametes) with half the number of chromosomes that are different, but derived from both the parent chromosomes. Meiosis is also known as *reduction division*. This is important for sexual reproduction where individual gametes from two parents (male and female) combine to form a new zygote cell developing into a new organism.

Ploidy level indicates how many sets of chromosomes (N) are present in a cell as mentioned below.

- *Haploid* (1N): single set of chromosomes. e.g.: sperm cell, egg cell.
- *Diploid* (2N): two sets of chromosomes. e.g.: body cells
- *Tetraploid* (4N): four sets of chromosomes. e.g.: plants, tobacco.
- *Polyploid* (many N): several sets of chromosomes. e.g.: sugarcane.

The basic differences between sexual and asexual reproduction are shown below.

Example of a diploid cell

Human cells contain 46 chromosomes or 23 pairs or two sets as in any other diploid organism. Among these, 22 pairs are called *autosomes* and two (X and Y or XX) are called *sex chromosomes*. The 23 pairs come from two parents. So in each pair of chromosome, one is paternal (from father) and another is maternal (from mother). These pairs are called **homologous chromosomes** or homologs (i.e. similar but not identical). Each homologous chromosome has an equivalent copy or copies of a gene (coding for RNA or protein). These two forms of a gene are called **alleles**. During meiosis the chromosome number in the diploid cell (46) is halved into 23 chromosomes in the gametes.

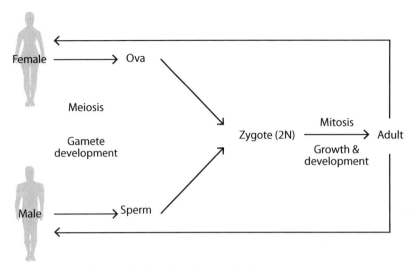

Figure 12-1. Sexual reproduction involves meiosis to generate gametes

Sexual Reproduction	Asexual Reproduction
gametes or reproductive cells	somatic or vegetative cells
needs meiosis and mitosis	mitosis is sufficient
two parent cells needed	single parent cell enough
chromosome number halved, then re-gained after fertilization	chromosome numbers and DNA sequence remains the same
greater variation in offspring due to recombination	highly homogeneous population due to identical progenies

11. Meiotic Cell Division

It occurs in two stages called Meiosis I and Meiosis II.

Meiosis I

Diploid cell (2N) enters Interphase I (DNA replication) → Prophase I → Metaphase I → Anaphase I → Telophase I → Cytokinesis I → 2 daughter cells (recombined homologs separated but the sister chromotaids are still attached)

Meiosis II

2 daughter cells enter Interphase II (No DNA replication) → Prophase II → Metaphase II → Anaphase II → Telophase II → Cytokinesis II → 4 haploid (1N) daughter cells (sister chromtids separated)

Meiosis 1

During meiosis I, the chromosomes replicate, homologous chromosomes cross over to exchange genetic material and the homologs separate.

Interphase I: Chromosomes replicate into two identical sister chromatids attached at centromere. The centrioles and other organelles also duplicate.

Prophase I: The most important stage in meiosis, Prophase I is more complex and takes more time to complete than the whole process of mitosis. It occupies about 90% of the time of meiosis. The condensed chromosome is attached to the nuclear envelope. The homologous chromosomes align themselves and come together to form _bivalents_ or _tetrads_ (four chromatids). Each gene is brought closer to its other counterpart (allele) in the other chromatids through _synapsis_. During synapsis, sections of homologous chromosomes overlap (_crossing over_) and homologous DNA is exchanged (_recombination_). The X-shaped regions of crossing over are called _chiasmata_. This genetic exchange between maternal and paternal chromosomes is a major source of variation among offspring. Later in Prophase i, the nuclear membrane dissolves, centrioles move apart, and spindle fibers form.

Metaphase I: Bivalent chromosomes (tetrads) align themselves in the middle of the cell along the _metaphase plate_. The kinetochore fibers attached to the centromere of each pair of recombined sister chromatids point to one pole. Homologous chromosomes are randomly assorted during this alignment, contributing to genetic variation.

Anaphase I: Individual pairs of sister chromatids separate from each other and go to opposite poles. The sister chromatids are still attached to each other.

Telophase I and **Cytokinesis I:** After the sister chromatids move to opposite poles, nuclear envelope may form and the cleavage furrow deepens to divide the cell. In plant cells, the cell plate forms.

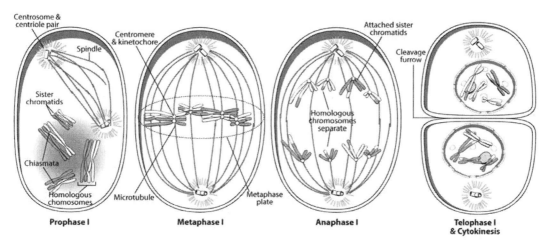

Figure 12-2. Meiosis I

Meiosis II

During meiosis II, the two daughter cells divide again but without DNA replication, producing four haploid cells.

Interphase II or Interkinesis is sometimes seen but no DNA replication happens.

Meiosis II: This is similar to mitosis without DNA replication. Sister chromatids separate during the Meiosis II.

Prophase II: If nucleus and nucleolus are present, they disappear and spindle fibers appear.

Metaphase II: The sister chromatids align on the metaphase plate. The kinetochore fibers pointing to opposite poles are attached at the centromere.

Anaphase II: Centromeres of the sister chromatids finally separate and indi-

vidual chromosomes (1N) finally move towards opposite ends.
Telophase II and **Cytokinesis II:** Nuclei begin to form around the chromosomes. Cleavage furrow or cell plate separates the new daughter cells.

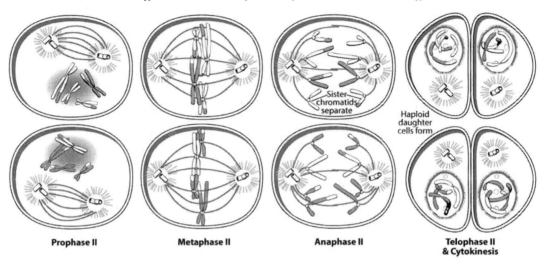

Prophase II	Metaphase II	Anaphase II	Telophase II & Cytokinesis

Figure 12-3. Meiosis II

Differences between Mitosis and Meiosis

Mitosis	Meiosis
One major division	Two major divisions
DNA replicate before each division	DNA replicate before meiosis I only
Chromosome number remains same	Chromosome number reduced to half
Daughter cells genetically identical (2N)	Daughter cells related but different (1N)
No synapsis, tetrads, or crossing over	Synapsis of tetrads leads to crossing over and recombination
Homologs and sister chromatids separate during anaphase; each cell receives and identical set	Homologs separate in anaphase I; sister chromatids separate in anaphase II
Two daughter cells	Four daughter cells

III. Causes of Genetic Variation in Sexual Reproduction

1. **Crossing over: During prophase I** the homologous chromosomes overlap each others and exchange genetic material resulting in recombination.
2. **Independent assortment of chromosomes:** In metaphase I, chromosomes separate independently; if there are 23 pairs of chromosomes, there are 2^{23} (8.3886 x 10^6 or ~8 million) possible combinations.
3. **Random fertilization:** If each sperm and egg cell coming from two different parents has a random chance of combining, it means 8.3886 x 10^6 x 8.3886 x 10^6 combinations, or 70.3686 x 10^{13}, or about seventy billion possible combinations for the offspring.

In addition to these variations, mutations accumulate in the DNA in both sexual and asexual reproduction.

13. INTRODUCTION TO GENETICS

Concepts

- Genes are units of inheritance as per Mendel and are passed on from one generation to the next.
- Alleles are alternate forms of a gene and exists as pairs in diploid organisms.
- There is no blending of traits from parents to offspring but discrete passing of specific genes corresponding to specific characteristics.
- Some alleles are linked and some are unlinked in their inheritance pattern.

Outline

I. Basic genetic terms
II. Mendel's laws of inheritance
III. Complexities of genetic expression
IV. Mendelian inheritance of human genetic disorders

1. Basic Genetic Terms

The basic foundations of classical genetics were established by Johann Gregor Mendel with his papers, published in 1866, but only recognized in early 1900s. With the current knowledge of classical and molecular genetics (studied at DNA level) we can understand the basic mechanisms of inheritance much better than few decades ago. The relationship between some of the terms used in genetics can be summed up in this diagram.

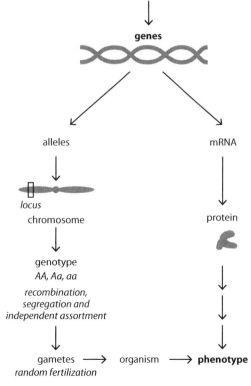

Figure 13-1. Flow of genetic information

DNA: deoxyribonucleic acid; basic genetic material containing 4 nucleotides; encodes information to make RNA and protein. The basic details are explained in chapter 5 on biological molecules and chapter 16 on DNA structure.

Genes: the unit of heredity according to classical genetics, based on the expression of a specific trait in successive generations of an organism. These genes may not have been isolated and characterized. It is sometimes used to refer to a locus. It is not exactly the same as in molecular genetics where gene is a particular DNA with a unique sequence which codes for a protein or RNA. Such genes may be 0.1 to 15 kilobases (kb) long.

Alleles: alternate forms of a gene, responsible for a particular trait, present in two different chromosomes which are derived from mother and father. These alleles may code for the same protein with slightly different amino acid sequences and may result in different traits. The alleles may be exchanged during meiosis in the crossing over and recombination process.

Locus (pl. loci)**:** the location of a gene or few genes on a chromosome, sometimes used interchangeably with gene, may be as long as 50 to 100 kb. Genes coding for different traits may exist close to each other on a locus and are less likely to be separated during recombination (*linked genes*/loci). Chromosomes are mapped with specific genes based on the frequency of recombination of known genes.

Chromosomes: contain several (hundreds of) loci each; exist as loosely dispersed chromatin (DNA + proteins) in interphase and condense into visible chromosomes during cell division.

Genotype: the assorted collection of various genes in the chromosomes, represented by capital or small letters to notate dominant and recessive alleles respectively, e.g.: AA, Aa, bb, etc.

Phenotype: a physical trait, physiological condition or biochemical aspect determined by the genes at the molecular level according to its genotype. E.g.: eye color (physical), sickle cell anemia (physiological) and herbicide resistant enzyme (biochemical).

Homozygous: an organism with a pair of identical alleles for a particular gene in both the homologous chromosomes, e.g.: AA, aa, BB, bb.

Heterozygous: an organism with mixed allele pairs for a particular gene, e.g.: Aa, Bb. An organism may be homozygous for one gene and heterozygous for another.

Dominant allele: The allele of a gene that is expressed under both homozygous and heterozygous condition due to the DNA sequence of the particular gene and the nature of the protein coded by such gene. Dominant allele is denoted in capital letters, e.g.: AA, BB, CC.

Recessive allele: The allele of a gene that is expressed only under homozygous condition, e.g.: aa, bb, cc. Again, an organism may contain a dominant allele for one gene and recessive for another.

Based on the genotype, an organism can be homozygous dominant (AA) or homozygous recessive (aa) or it can be heterozygous (Aa).

11. Mendel's Laws of Inheritance

Reasons for Mendel's Success:

1. *Quantitative approach*: He used a mathematical approach to a biological problem. This is one reason why his results were not appreciated or acknowledged immediately.

2. *Good model system*: Peas are easy to grow and hybridize to monitor

inheritance.

3. *Selection of traits or phenotypes*: He chose phenotypes that are easy to study such as pod color (green/yellow), seed shape (round/wrinkled), stem length (tall/dwarf) etc. which are all measurable and distinct.

Pure bred (homozygous) varieties (parents, F_0) are crossed by hybridization (fertilizing one plant's stigma with another plant's pollen). Medel observed the first generation (F_1) and back crossed the F_1 with parents or self to study the segregation at second generation (F_2).

A. Law of segregation

Allele pairs segregate (separate) during gamete formation and the paired condition is restored by the random fusion of gametes at fertilization.

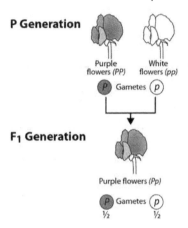

Example
Mendel selected pure bred pea varieties with either spherical seeds or dented seeds. When he crossed them and obtained first progenies (F_1) he obtained 253 plants all of which had spherical seeds. He self-pollinated all of the F_1 plants and found that 3/4th of the F_2 progenies had spherical seeds and 1/4th had dented seeds. The ratio was 3:1 for these two traits. This cross is called a monohybrid cross.

From these results of restoring the dented feature, he formulated the particulate theory of the "gene" as discrete units of heredity which separate during the formation of gametes and can be mixed by fertilizing two gametes to restore the phenotype. The units of heredity are present as alleles in the gametes which segregate during gamete formation and he demon-

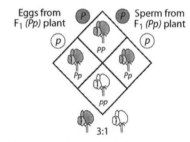

Figure 13.2 Monohybrid cross

strated this by breeding the peas as shown in the figure on next page.

A **test cross** is done by hybridizing a parent of unknown genotype with a known homozygous recessive parent to find out if the unknown genotype is homozygous or heterozygous.

If the unknown parent is homozygous:
aa x AA = all F_1 will be heterozygous (Aa)
If the unknown parent is heterozygous:
aa x Aa = half of F_1 will be homozygous (aa) and other half heterozygous (Aa)

B. Law of independent assortment

Law: The segregation of each allele pair is independent of other allele pairs. The individual allele pairs need to be located on separate loci, far from each other to allow independent assortment during gamete formation.

Example

This can be explained by considering two different traits coded by two allele pairs. This is referred to as a dihybrid cross. Spherical (S) and yellow (Y) seeds are dominant traits with their corresponding recessive alleles for dented (ss) and green (yy) seeds phenotype. If we cross a parent which is homozygous dominant for both (SSYY) with spherical yellow seeds with another parent which is homozygous recessive (ssyy) for both alleles with dented green seeds, one can expect a completely heterozygous condition (SsYy) with spherical yellow seeds in F_1 generation. When these seeds are self-crossed, the following probabilities are observed as shown below.

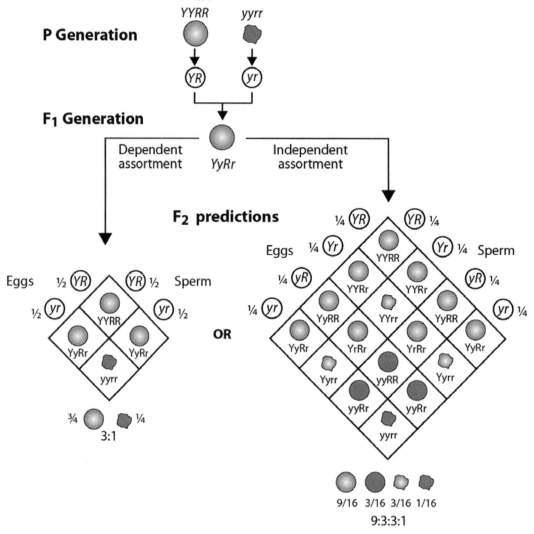

Figure 13.3 Dihybrid cross

These probabilities in a dihybrid cross can also be obtained by using the rule of multiplication (to determine the chances of two independent events occurring together).

Probabilities of a seed being

- yellow is 3/4 or spherical is 3/4 (dominant traits as we saw in monohybrid cross),
- both yellow and spherical is 3/4 x 3/4 = 9/16,
- green is 1/4 or dented is 1/4 (because they are recessive traits as we saw

in monohybrid cross) and
- both yellow and spherical is 1/4 x 1/4 = 1/16.

For a combination of dominant and recessive phenotypes (also called re-combinant phenotypes),
- yellow and dented is 3/4 x 1/4 = 3/16 and
- spherical and green is 3/4 x 1/4 = 3/16.

The overall ratio of different phenotypes such as yellow and spherical: yellow and dented: green and spherical: green and dented is 9:3:3:1.

This type of segregation proved that alleles can segregate independent of each other and recombine to make new phenotypes.

III. Complexities of Genetic Inheritance

Intermediate inheritance or incomplete dominance

The homozygotes have a particular phenotype, and the heterozygotes have an intermediate phenotype meaning that no single gene is completely dominant. E.g.: Snapdragon flowers with red (RR) and white (rr) color flowers are crossed the F_1 generation will have all pink flowers (Rr) showing intermediate inheritance. When the F_1 is selfed the F_2 generation will have a mixture of red (RR), pink (Rr) and white (rr) flowers in a ratio of 1:2:1.

Codominance

Both phenotypes are expressed at about equal levels by the expression of two types of proteins by two alleles. E.g.: People with the blood type AB will express both the proteins for types A and B. The white clover leaf has two patterns which are present in different homozygous conditions; both the patterns will appear in the heterozygous condition.

Pleiotropy

One gene or allele codes for more than one phenotype. E.g.: albino individuals lack pigments in skin, eye and hair showing the effect of a single mutation in one locus causing varied effects. In severe diseases such as sickle cell anemia or cystic fibrosis, several symptoms can be traced to one or a few genes; this may be due to the nature of an individual gene affecting many phenotypes or several genes in one locus being responsible for the varied effects.

Epistasis: One gene interferes with the expression of another gene. Several pairs of alleles may interact to affect a single phenotype. For example, when several enzymes interact in a common biosynthetic pathway, if one enzyme is defective, it affects the others. E.g.: skin color in mice is affected by two pairs of alleles, and if one locus (pair of alleles) is homozygous recessive, mice are always albino irrespective of the other locus.

Multiple genes

Some genes exist in more than two forms. E.g.: skin color in humans is determined by three genes (A, B, C). The dominant alleles of the genes result in dark skin and recessive genes in light skin. Based on the combination of the three allele pairs, the skin color varies from light (aa,bb,cc) to dark color (AA,BB,CC). Many complex traits such as height, intelligence or weight are determined by multiple genes (polygenic traits).

Sex-linked inheritance
The phenotypes affected by genes located on sex chromosomes are expressed depending on the sex of the individuals. The XX (female) and XY (male) system is followed in humans and many animals. However, there are other systems such as ZW (female) and ZZ (male) in birds. The genes present on only one sex chromosome, for example, X in male (XY), is referred to as hemizygous condition. There are several sex linked traits such as baldness, hemophilia and muscular dystrophy.

Maternal inheritance
The genes present in mitochondria and chloroplasts are always inherited maternally. Only nuclear genes are carried on from one gamete to another in males, and the mitochondria and chloroplasts present in the egg are copied in the zygote (after fertilization) and passed on to next generation. E.g.: stem coloration in the four-o'clock plant is due to the chlorophyll content determined by chloroplast genes derived from female parent.

Environmental effect on gene expression
The influence of environment on gene expression results in wider variation especially in traits controlled by multiple genes. E.g.: skin color determined by three alleles is affected further by sunlight intensifying the melanin pigmentation. Other examples of include the influence of nutrition and exercise on weight or height. Hydrangea flowers may be blue if grown in acidic soil or pink in alkaline soil.

IV. Mendelian Inheritance of Human Genetic Disorders

There are several genetic disorders that are inherited based on the same principles Mendel proposed. Since we cannot do breeding experiments with humans, we use pedigree analyses to study the inheritance pattern of a particular character and asses if they are dominantly or recessively inherited. For example, if a trait is recessive, it will be expressed only if the person showing the phenotype is homozygous. If such a homozygous recessive individual marries someone without that trait (unknown genotype), we can tell if the other person is homozygous dominant or heterozygous based on the segregation of traits in their children. If all of them do not have that trait, the other person is homozygous dominant or if some children show the trait, that person is heterozygous as illustrated below.

Parent 1: homozygous recessive and with the phenotype (aa)
Parent 2: unknown genotype and normal phenotype (??)

If all children are normal without the recessive phenotype, parent 2 is AA. If some children show the same phenotype as Parent 1, then the parent 2 has heterozygous genotype (Aa).

On the other hand, if a trait is dominant, the parents will show the trait and will pass it on to all the first generation children if they are homozygous and to some of the children if they are heterozygous, assuming the other parent is homozygous recessive (no trait).

Pedigree analysis is illustrated in the following example of a recessively inherited trait (cystic fibrosis). Let us denote the alleles as CC or cc.

If the parent is	Homozygous dominant	Heterozygous	Homozygous recessive
Genotype	CC	Cc	cc
Phenotype	No disease	No disease but a carrier	Disease
Children (F1)	All children will be normal, irrespective of other parent	Some children will show the trait if the other parent is cc or Cc	If other parent is CC, no children will show the trait, but if Cc or cc, some will should the trait

Inheritance of selected traits in humans

Selected examples of recessively and dominantly inherited disorders in humans are listed below.

Recessive	Dominant
No freckles	Freckles
5 fingers	6 fingers
No widow's peak	Widow's peak
Albinism	Achondroplasia
Cystic fibrosis	Alzheimer's disease
Tay Sachs disease	Huntington's disease
Sickle cell anemia	Hypercholesterolemia
Phenylketonuria	
Galactosemia	

The occurrence of a particular trait in human populations varies based on its effect on survival and reproduction. If a trait is homozygous and lethal (e.g.: cystic fibrosis (recessive) or hypercholesterolemia (dominant)), the individual will not live to the reproductive stage to pass it on. However, if the individual is heterozygous and the disease is not severe, they will serve as a carrier and pass the genes to the next generation. In general recessive allleles are more prevalent whther the trait has a deleterious effect of not.

There are several traits that are determined by multiple genes. Such polygenic traits show wide variations in the phenotype and are relatively complex to analyze by simple Mendelian inheritance. E.g.: heart disease, cancer, diabetes, schizophrenia, manic depression and alcoholism. In addition, other traits such as height, weight, skin color and general behavior are regulated by multiple genes. Environmental and social conditions also have significant influence on the expression of these phenotypes.

Detection of genetic disorders

The early detection of genetic disorders is very important for the survival of the infant or possible children. If the parents are carriers of specific genes for a genetic disorder, genetic counseling may help to decide the chances of having a healthy child. Even in such cases, the parents need to make a decision to go ahead with pregnancy, even if the chances are low.

Parents can also perform early detection tests such as **chorionic villus sampling (CVS) or amniocentesis** to check for the presence of a particular allele in the fetus. There are risks (1-2%) associated with these invasive tests. At later stages, they can perform an *ultrasound* to confirm that the child is anatomically normal and healthy. Also, they can perform some *blood tests* of the mother to check for the presence of proteins indicative of potential problems with the fetus.

However, it may sometimes be late to decide about the fetus if the results are known after the first trimester. Since most of these tests are done from weeks 14-20, it becomes a very difficult situation for the parents to decide on the alternatives. Hence, early **genetic counseling** is preferred to understand the risks, methods of detection and possible treatments. Occasionally, the in vitro fertilized embryos can be screened for the healthy ones and then implanted in the mother's uterus for a successful pregnancy which will avoid later complications. Such tests are not yet commonly used but may become common in the future. However, this raises several ethical implications of parents to continue with the preganancy or not or to choose healthy embryos to implant.

14. DNA STRUCTURE AND REPLICATION

Concepts

- Genetic material, DNA, stores information and can be replicated.
- DNA forms a double helix with a ribose-phosphate backbone and nitrogenous bases making H-bonds.
- Replication of DNA is semiconservative and involves several proteins.
- Repairing the mistakes in DNA replication or any damages caused by other factors is critical to preventing mutations.

Outline

I.   Search for the Genetic Material
II. DNA Structure
III. DNA Replication
IV. DNA Repair

I.   Search for the Genetic Material

Proteins were initially considered to be the genetic material due to the diversity of their composition (20 amino acids) and function. The presence of proteins in chromosomes further strengthened this notion. Nucleic acids were considered to be too simple (only four bases) to carry on the hereditary function. However, the following experiments proved that DNA is the material that stores genetic information and passes it on from generation to generation.

A. Evidence of DNA transforming bacteria

In 1928, Fredrick Griffith studied different strains of Streptococcus pneumoniae (the bacteria that causes pneumonia in humans). He used an S-strain (smooth; has a smooth polysaccharide coating), which can cause disease in mice, and an R-strain (rough; no coating), which did not cause the disease when injected in mice. He heat killed the S-strain which also did not cause any disease. However, a mixture of heat-killed S-strain and R-strain caused disease when injected together. Griffith concluded that the heat-killed S-strain transformed the R-strain by transferring the "**genetic principle**." Even though one can argue that proteins are denatured during heating and only DNA can renature and transform, this experiment did not conclusively prove that it was DNA and not protein that transformed the R-strain.

Later in 1944, Oswald Avery, Colin McLeod and Maclyn McCarty isolated extracts from the heat-killed S-strain and treated them with proteases (degrade proteins), RNases (degrade RNA) or DNases (degrade DNA). Then he mixed the treated extracts with R-strain and showed only the protease- and RNase treated extracts were able to transform the R-strain into a disease-causing strain. This was the first in vitro **transformation** of one bacterial strain by introducing DNA from another bacterial strain. This was a major milestone in molecular biology that demonstrated DNA was the genetic material and that genetic transformation with DNA is possible. However, this was not taken seriously until further evidence came from an independent experiment explained next.

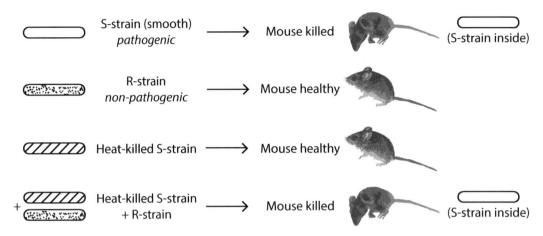

Figure 14-1. Transformation of bacteria to become pathogenic

B. Evidence of viral DNA programming bacteria

Bacteriophages are viruses-infecting bacteria. Viruses contain a DNA or RNA genome with a protein capsid (envelope). In 1952, Alfred Hershey and Martha Chase conducted a new experiment using a T_2 bacteriophage which was known to inject part of its contents into bacteria to program the cells to make more viruses. Hershey and Chase wanted to find out if the genetic material that is injected into bacteria was DNA or protein.

First they cultured two batches of the T_2 phage separately in media containing ^{35}S and ^{32}P to label proteins and DNA respectively. Then they isolated the phages and used them to infect bacteria cultured without any radioisotope. After infection, they mixed the contents vigorously in a kitchen blender to shake off the phages from the bacteria. The mixture was then centrifuged to pellet the bacteria and retain the phages in supernatant. The pellet fraction (bacteria) contained most of the ^{32}P and the supernatant contained most of the ^{35}S, indicating that DNA was the genetic material injected into bacterial cells to program the cells to make more viruses.

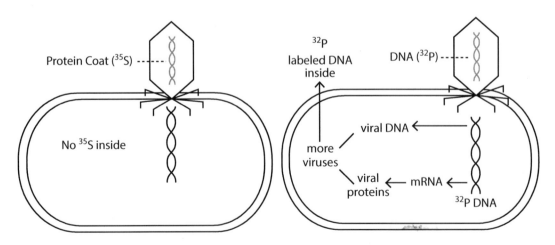

Figure 14-2. Use of 35 S and 32 P to label DNA and proteins respectively in the phage

C. Other supporting evidence

In addition to these results described earlier, other circumstantial evidence including; (1) **Erwin Chargaff**'s report in **1950** that different species contained different compositions of DNA (GC content) and the percent of A was equal to that of T and the percent of G was equal to that of C. (2) that chromosomes go through duplication during cell division also supported the hypothesis that DNA is the genetic material and carries hereditary information.

Once it was known that DNA was the genetic material, scientists were rushing to elucidate the structure of DNA and to understand its replication process. Chargaff had also reported that the amounts of adenine and thymine were approximately equal, and the amounts of guanine and cytosine were approximately equal. These reports were helpful in elucidating the structure of DNA.

II. DNA Structure

A. Basic structure of DNA

The fact that DNA contained nucleotide bases connected by covalent bonds in a polymer was known in 1950 but the three-dimensional structure and the mechanism of DNA replication were not yet known. Several scientists were making strong efforts to confirm the structure of DNA.

Linus Pauling in California had developed models of protein structures and he proposed that DNA was a triple helix. Maurice Wilkins and Rosalind Franklin in King's College London were studying the X-ray crystallography structure of DNA. James Watson from America and Francis Crick of England were working on the chemistry of DNA in Cambridge University, London using chemical models of the bases to develop a three dimensional structure.

During their investigation Watson visited Rosalind Franklin and saw the X-ray crystallography pictures of DNA. Those pictures, containing spots and smudges due to X-ray diffraction through cross sections of a DNA strand, gave insight into the possible structure of DNA. Two major pieces of information obtained from the pictures were that the diameter of DNA was 2 nm and the bases were stacked perpendicular to the strand with a distance of 0.34 nm between the bases.

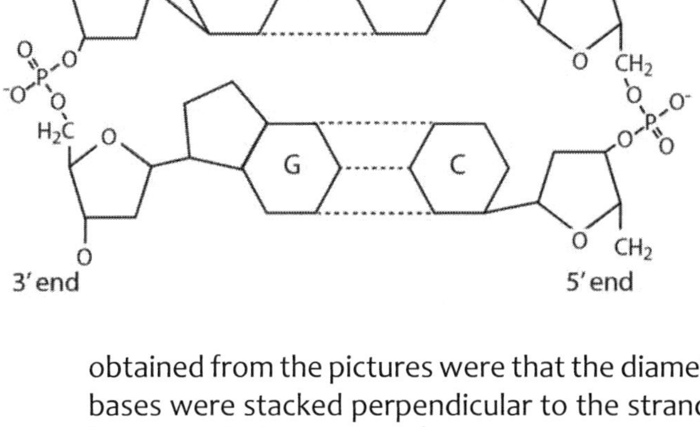

Figure 14-3. **H-Bonding of the complementary basepairs in DNA**

Later, Watson and Crick used the chemical models and constructed the double helix structure of DNA by trying different possible combinations. The results from the findings of Watson & Crick, Maurice Wilkins and Rosalind Franklin were published in **1953** in Nature.

The main features of the DNA double helix are summarized below:
1. DNA consists of two strands that are H-bonded together with a width of 2 nm.
2. The two strands turn right to make a right-handed helix (turns clockwise, when looked through cross section). The strands are like the ropes of a ladder with the bases making the rungs.
3. The hydrophilic sugar-phosphate is on the outside of helix. The negatively charged P-groups make DNA soluble in aqueous solution.
4. The hydrophobic nitrogenous bases are stacked inside in a perpendicular manner to the strand. The distance between two base pairs is 0.34 nm. There are 10 base pairs per turn.
5. Adenine pairs with thymine with 2 H-bonds and guanine pairs with cytosine with 3 H-bonds. This is referred to as *complementary base pairing* and satisfies Charagaff's finding that the cellular ratios of A:T and G:C are equal (*Chargaff's rule*).
6. The two strands run in opposite directions i.e. have *anti-parallel orientation*. DNA starts with a phosphate group attached to the 5th C of ribose (5') and the other end has a -OH group attached to the 3rd C of ribose (3').
7. The helical turns make a major groove and a minor groove between the adjacent turns.
8. DNA stores information in its sequence of bases (four bases with infinite possibilities of various sequence and lengths).
9. DNA replication is *semiconservative*. New copy is made from a template DNA with high specificity.

Later in 1962, Watson, Crick and Wilkins were awarded a Nobel Prize for elucidating the three-dimensional structure of DNA. Rosalind Franklin had passed away before this time, and the Nobel Prize is not awarded posthumously.

B. Different forms of DNA

Supercoiling
The double helix of DNA coils onto itself resulting in supercoiled DNA. This occurs in circular DNA (plasmids, bacterial chromosome, chloroplast and mitochondrial DNA) and linear eukaryotic chromosomes. Supercoiling is important to keep the DNA compact in the cell and during DNA replication. (Circular DNA may also be open.)

DNA is present mostly in the double-stranded form (dsDNA). However, single stranded DNA (ssDNA) is present in viral genomes. The double strandedness of DNA contributes to its stability and allows for proof-reading. The major helical forms of DNA and their features are listed in the following table.

Feature	A-DNA	B-DNA	Z-DNA
Helix Diameter	2.55 nm	2.37 nm	1.84 nm
Rise/base	2.3 Å	3.4 Å	3.8 Å
Turn	right	right	left
Base pairs per turn	11	10.4	12
Occurrence	dehydrated form	most common form of in cells	short oligonucleotides GCGCGC

Denaturing/renaturing DNA

Since the double helix of DNA is bonded with H-bonds they can be separated by heating or exposing to alkaline conditions. The same DNA can be renatured to its original form (*hybridization*; they rejoin due to complementary basepairing) by gradual cooling or neutralizing the alkaline solution with a mild acid. This mechanism is extensively used to study DNA.

III. DNA Replication

A. DNA replication is semiconservative

Semiconservative refers to the fact that half of a newly-made DNA is the old template. In other words, one strand is used as a template to make new strand based on complementary base pairing rules (A:T and G:C). First *in vitro* DNA synthesis was performed by Arthur Kornberg in 1953 using a template DNA, DNA polymerase and four nucleotides. If any one nucleotide is missing DNA synthesis will stop. This was done in a test tube without any cells, demonstrating that DNA can replicate itself.

However, the semiconservative mechanism was proven by an experiment by Matthew Meselson and Franklin Stahl in 1957. They used ^{14}N (lighter) and ^{15}N (heavier) isotopes to distinguish the old DNA template and new DNA made from the template. First they grew bacteria in a medium containing ^{15}N (in ammonium chloride) for 17 generations which resulted in the nitrogenous bases in DNA labeled with ^{15}N.

They collected bacterial samples from this culture (sample 1) and then inoculated into a medium containing ^{14}N. They allowed it to replicate once (20 minutes) and collected the second sample after one DNA replication (sample 2). The bacteria were allowed to replicate once more (40 minutes) to undergo another DNA replication. The third sample was collected after 60 minutes (sample 3). They isolated DNA from these samples using cesium chloride density gradient centrifugation which can separate a solution according to the density of each DNA (the heavier the DNA, the lower the DNA band in the centrifuge tube). The following results were obtained:

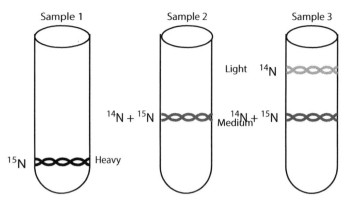

Figure 14-4.   **Banding of different DNA samples based on the density**

These results indicated that the new DNA strand synthesized in sample 2 after one DNA replication/cell division is a combination of old (^{15}N-DNA) and new (^{14}N-DNA) DNA strands. If both strands were new, one would expect two bands of ^{15}N and ^{14}N DNA strands. This proved that DNA replicates semiconservatively, i.e.: half old template and half newly-made DNA.

B. Mechanism of DNA replication

DNA replication starts in a place called the *origin of replication* which is a location on DNA molecule with a specific sequence that is recognized by enzymes involved in DNA replication. As we saw earlier, bacterial chromosomes and plasmids contain a single origin of replication whereas eukaryotic chromosomes contain multiple origins of replication. The bacterial origin of replication is about 245 bp long. In eukaryotes, the origin of replication is not that well defined.

DNA replication in the cell is complex and requires the concerted action of several proteins as mentioned above. Under in vitro conditions, a DNA template, DNA primer (short oligonucleotide), Mg^{++}, DNA polymerase, dNTPS in a suitable buffer (to maintain optimum salt, pH condition) will be enough to synthesize DNA.

The proteins that play a major role in DNA replication are listed below.

Protein	Size (kDa)	Function
1. Topoisomerase I	97	relaxes the supercoiled DNA
2. Helicase	300	unwinds the double helix into single stranded DNA (ssDNA)
3. SSB	74	single-stranded DNA binding protein; stablizes the ssDNA
4. Primase	60	synthesizes RNA primers
5. DNA polymerase I	103	erases RNA primers and fills in the gaps
6. DNA polymerase III holoenzyme	750-900	DNA replication, proof reading and repair
7. DNA ligase	74	covalently joins free 3' and 5' ends of two DNA strands
8. DNA gyrase	400	introduces supercoiling in DNA

DNA Replication in vivo

The diagram on the next page gives an overview of DNA replication. Please note that the picture is not to scale in terms of relative dimensions of different sub-diagrams. The RNA primers shown are longer than what is shown here and the enzymes are much bigger than the DNA strand itself. DNA replication starts at the origin of replication and proceeds bidirectionally. The replication bubble consists of two replication forks joined together which expand wider as the DNA replication progresses.

Initiation
- Supercoiling relaxed at the **origin of replication (ORI)** by topoisomerase (single origin in prokaryotes and multiple origins in eukaryotes).
- Relaxed DNA helix opened to make a replication fork by **helicase.**
- Resulting single stranded DNA is stabilized by **single stranded DNA binding (SSB) proteins.**
- **Primase** makes an RNA primer (providing a free 3'-OH group for the DNA polymerase to use) to start the new DNA synthesis.

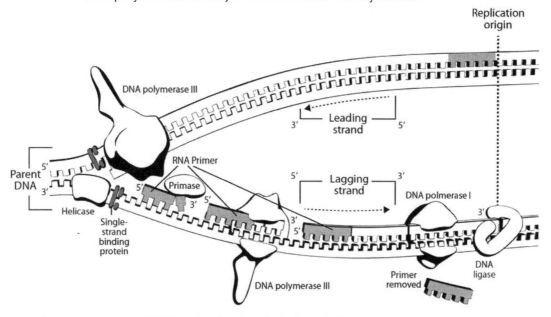

Figure 14-5.　　**DNA Replication fork including all the enzymes and primers.**

Elongation
- **DNA polymerase III** (a complex protein) binds to the DNA template + RNA-primer and adds nucleotides complementary to the template strand (at a rate of about 1000 nucleotides/sec in prokaryotes).
- **New DNA synthesis occurs in the 5' to 3' direction** on a templete that runs in the 3' to 5' direction. This is due to the nature of the enzyme DNA polymerase, which links new deoxy-nucleoside triphosphates (dNTPs) to the 3'-OH group of the growing strand. Also, the H-bonding in the base pairing works only if the new strand runs in the opposite direction of the template DNA.
- A **leading strand** is synthesized continuously from 5' to 3' based on the template.
- Since the opposite strand is not open to continue DNA synthesis from 5' to 3' direction, DNA is synthesized in small fragments (100-200 bas-

es in eukaryotes and 1000-2000 in prokaryotes), called **Okazaki fragments**. This strand is the **lagging strand** (made slowly after the *leading strand*).

- Once the new DNA strand is synthesized, DNA polymerase III proofreads it and removes errors. **DNA polymerase I** removes the RNA primer and completes the DNA strand.
- Once the small fragments are completed, DNA ligase joins the two ends of DNA strands to complete DNA replication. DNA gyrase facilitates supercoiling the DNA to compact the chromosomes into nucleosomes.

IV. DNA *repair*

It is very important for cells to correct errors in DNA replication or any damage caused to the DNA after replication (e.g.: by carcinogenic chemicals, x-rays, etc.) because such errors may be fatal. Mistakes must be repaired before the DNA can function and replicate again. If left uncorrected, stable mutations result and may be passed on to the next generation of cells or organisms.

There are three major types of DNA repair mechanisms operating in the cell.

1. **Mismatch repair** is done to correct errors made during DNA replication. DNA polymerase III makes ~1 mistake in 10,000 base pairs. Then, it proofreads the newly-made DNA, removes the wrong bases and repairs the DNA to minimize the errors to 1 in a billion. These error corrections use the mismatch repair mechanism by checking complementary base pairing. E.g.: problem in mismatch repair causes colon cancer.

2. **Telomere repair or preservation** also occurs during DNA replication and it is catalysed by an enzyme called **telomerase** helps prevent the telomere from getting shortened after each cell cycle. Telomerase temporarily extends the telomere region to allow the RNA primer to bind for DNA replication and once it is replicated, the extended region annealed to the RNA primer is removed to maintain the same length of telomere. Telomerase is active in young organisms with actively growing cells and in cancer cells.

3. **Excision repair** occurs after a cell divides and is in the G_1 phase or G_2 phase. This damage is caused by carcinogens and mutagenic radiations altering the bases or making pyrimidine dimers (e.g.T-T). Such mutations are constantly monitored by over 50 different enzymes and corrected by excising the damaged strand of DNA (by an endonuclease) and making a new matching strand (by DNA polymerase and DNA ligase) in its place. E.g.: the disease xeroderma pigmentosum is caused by a lack of enzyme(s) involved in excision repair.

15. TRANSCRIPTION AND TRANSLATION

Concepts

- A gene is a linear segment of DNA that contains the information needed to synthesize or 'express' a particular gene product (RNA or protein).
- Gene expression involves two sequential steps: (1) transcription of mRNA from DNA; (2) translation of mRNA to produce a polypeptide.
- Transcription relies on complementary base-pairing to copy the nucleotide sequence information present in one strand of the double helix.
- Messenger RNAs are processed prior to translation. In eukaryotes, this includes the removal or splicing of introns and addition of 5' G-cap and 3' poly-A tail.
- Translation takes place in the ribosome and relies upon a highly conserved universal genetic code.
- Some newly synthesized polypeptides must undergo additional chemical modifications before they become mature, functional proteins.
- Mutations are changes in the genetic information encoded in DNA and may change the sequence of amino acids in the final protein product.

Outline

I.   Transcription
II. The Genetic Language and Mutations
III. Translation

1. Transcription

The central dogma of molecular biology originally proposed by Francis Crick states that DNA makes RNA makes protein.

A. RNA synthesis

RNA is synthesized in the 5' to 3' direction by RNA polymerase from a DNA template in the presence of nucleoside triphosphates (NTPs) and Mg^{++} in a suitable pH and salt condition. RNA polymerases do not need primers due to the nature of their active site. Knowing the structure of a gene and the factors involved in transcription are important to understanding transcription.

RNA polymerase acts in concert with several other proteins which bind DNA and affect transcription (trans-acting factors or simply *transcription factors*). The transcription factors recognize specific sequences on the DNA called *cis-acting elements*. These elements include, but are not limited to, the **promoter** and/or an enhancer or suppressor element. These are specific regions on the DNA which affect the amount, rate and accuracy of transcription. The promoter in eukaryotes consists of a TATA box (TATA-rich region ~10 bp), GC box (~35-40 bp) and CAAT box (~90-110 bp) on the sense/coding strand.

Promoters affect the accuracy and amount of transcription. The enhancer or suppressors are called regulatory regions, which, when bound by transcription factors, result in more active or less active transcription respectively.

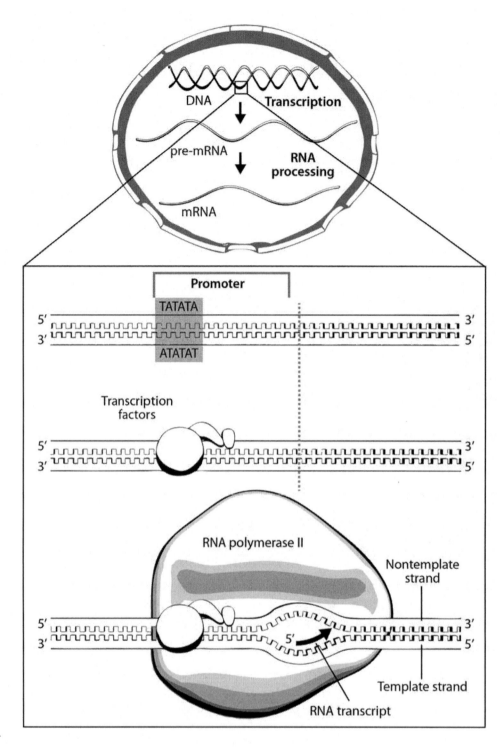

Figure 15-1. Flow of genetic information from DNA to RNA during transcription

Once the RNA polymerase + transcription factors bind to the promoter, they open the double helix and start to RNA transcription by incorporating NTPs (C U A G) complementary to the template DNA strand (G A T C). The opposite strand is not transcribed.

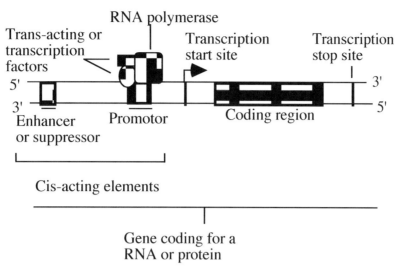

Figure 15-2. Structure of a gene with binding sites for transcription factors and RNA polymerase

Transcription proceeds at approximately 60 nucleotides per second and stops at the transcription stop site. The stop site is denoted by the sequence AATAAA in eukaryotes. One gene can be transcribed by several RNA polymerases simultaneously resulting in a bunch of mRNAs varying from longest to shortest mRNA generated from one DNA template.

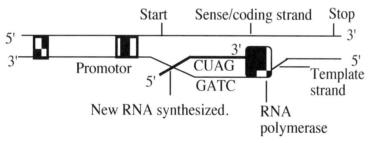

Figure 15-3. Transcription of new RNA strand

There are three types of RNA polymerases, which transcribe different RNA molecules. **RNA polymerase I** transcribes ribosomal RNA (rRNA); **RNA polymerase II** transcribes messenger RNA (mRNA); and **RNA polymerase III** transcribes transfer RNA (tRNA) and one type of rRNA. The differences among these RNAs are explained later in next section.

Differences between prokaryotes and eukaryotes
In prokaryotes, many genes are situated continuously in one operon (set of genes with one control element i.e. promoter/operator). Transcription results in a single transcript (mRNA) that codes for more than one protein. This is called **polycistronic,** i.e. many messages per transcription. Also, prokaryotes transcribe and translate simultaneously because there is no nuclear membrane to separate transcription and translation. Prokaryotes have only one type of RNA polymerase. Moreover, prokaryotic RNA does not go through any processing such as polyadenylation or intron (intervening sequences) removal before translation.

Eukaryotic transcription occurs in the nucleus, physically separate from the cytoplasm, where translation takes place. Also, eukaryotic genes are **mono-cistronic**, i.e.: one gene transcribed per transcription, each transcript coding for one protein. (Some viruses in eukaryotic cells have been shown to have polycistronic messages.) In addition, eukaryotic RNAs contain intervening sequences called **introns** which are removed and the expressed regions, called **exons** are spliced during RNA processing explained below. Eukaryotic RNA also goes through attachment of a poly-A tail + RNA and Guanine-cap.

B. RNA Processing

Eukaryotic RNA undergoes extensive processing inside nucleus before it leaves for translation in cytoplasm. The two major types of processing are given below.

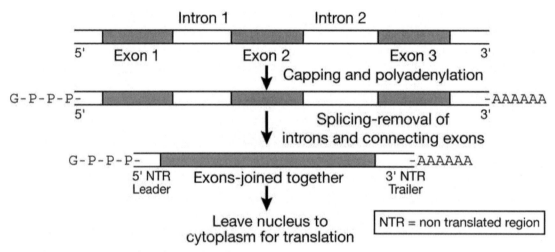

Figure 15-4. Processing of mRNA in eukaryotes

1. Capping and polyadenylation

After transcription, the phosphate group of a modified form of guanosine triphosphate (GTP) is added to the 5' end of RNA. This process is called *capping,* and it helps protect the mRNA and mark the 5' end as starting point for translation. At the 3' end, a stretch of polyAs (adenines) are added by an enzyme poly(A) polymerase. The length of polyA tail varies from 30 - 200 adenines. Poly(A) tail protects the mRNA from being degraded. However, only mRNAs are capped and polyadenylated to increase their stability. rRNAs and tRNAs do not go through polyadenylation and g-capping but they do sometimes go through the splicing process. PolyA+ RNA is not found in prokaryotes.

2. Splicing

Introns are intervening sequences that generally do not code for a protein. Very rarely, introns may code for a smaller, different protein. Exons are expressed regions coding for a protein or a segment of a protein. During splicing, introns are removed and exons are joined together. NTR refers to *non-translated regions* which are present in processed RNA at 5' and 3' ends but they do not code for protein. Some RNAs splice themselves, and they are called **autocatalytic RNAs**. This process is called **self-splicing**. In other RNAs, splicing occurs in a complex called a **splicesome**, made up of small nuclear

RNAs (snRNAs), small nuclear ribonucleoproteins (**snRNPs**-called "**snurps**") and proteins. Almost all eukaryotic RNAs undergo splicing and further processing. A few genes lack introns, and they undergo different processing.

V. The Genetic Language and Mutations

Initially, the relationship between DNA, RNA and proteins was not clearly understood. In 1909, English Physician Archibald Garrod studied the disease alkaptonuria in which the chemical alkapton accumulates in the urine, making the urine turn black upon exposure to air. Garrod suggested that such errors of metabolism are due to a lack of specific enzymes involved in the pathway and could be inherited genetically. However, this was not considered seriously until further evidence on genes and enzymes was obtained.

A. One gene-one polypeptide hypothesis

Biochemists accumulated evidence that many metabolic reactions are performed by enzymes in 1900s. In the 1940s George Beadle and Edward Tatum were studying mutants of a fungus *Neurospora crassa.* The normal *Neurospora,* grown on a minimal medium containing defined minerals and no other nutritional supplements, are called **wild type or prototrophs.** Beadle and Tatum generated mutants of *Neurospora* that could not grow on minimal medium without additional supplements (amino acids or sugars) by treating the fungus with X-rays. Such nutritional mutants are called **auxotrophs,** meaning they need auxillory (additional) nourishment to survive.

Predicted

Genes		A		B		C	
		↓		↓		↓	
Enzymes		a		b		c	
Pathway	Precursor	⟶	Ornithine	⟶	Citrulline	⟶	Arginine

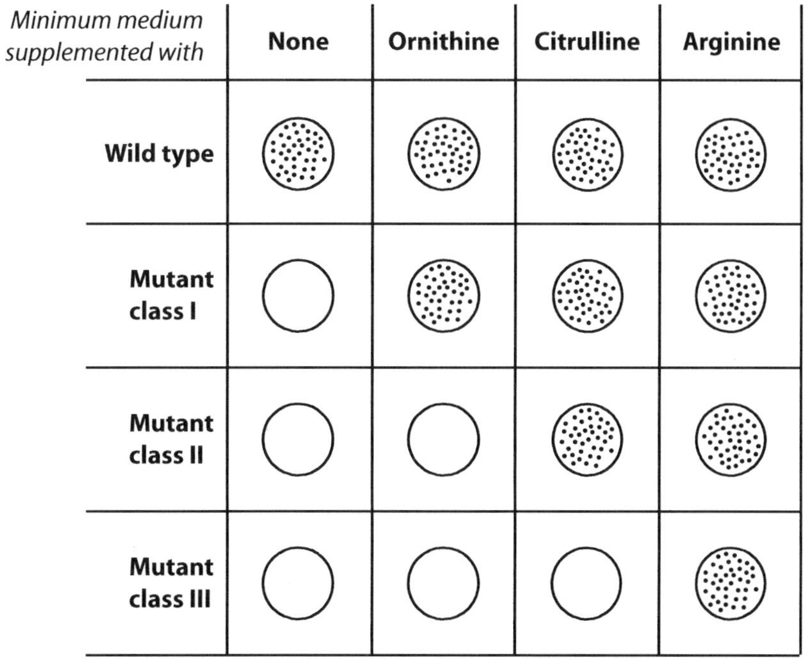

Figure 15-5. Experiment to test one gene -one enzyme hypothesis

In one study, (as shown in Figure 15-5) the mutants were selected by plating them on minimal media alone and with supplements in the biosynthesis of arginine. A filled circle means the fungus is growing and open circle means the fungus is not growing. The pathway of making arginine was fairly well known except for the enzymes; precursor → ornithine → citrulline → arginine. So, if a mutant survives on media with a specific intermediate of this pathway, say citrulline, (and not with ornithine) it means that mutant can continue the pathway beyond citrulline and there is a mutation in the enzyme making citrulline. Since they predicted three genes encoding three enzymes in this pathway and they obtained three classes of mutants, i.e. one for each gene and enzyme, they proved the **one-gene, one-enzyme hypothesis**. Based on these results, Beadle and Tatum concluded that one enzyme is coded by one gene and any mutation in that gene will result in a mutant enzyme. This one gene-one-enzyme hypothesis was later modified to the **one-gene, one-polypepetide hypothesis** to reflect the fact that not all proteins are enzymes.

B. The genetic language

The central dogma of molecular biology proposed by Crick was resolved by the results of several experiments.

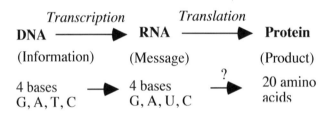

The first question was to understand how information is communicated from DNA to protein. The messenger hypothesis by Crick, Sydney Brenner and Francois Jacob proposed that DNA is first copied (transcribed) into a messenger RNA (mRNA), which is translated into protein using adapters (transfer RNA; tRNA). The possibility of a coding system (using codons) was obvious because DNA and RNA have only 4 bases and a protein can be made from 20 different amino acids. This was resolved by simple logic as follows:

> If one base codes for one amino acid, it can code for only 4 amino acids; if two bases code for one amino acid, only $4^2 = 16$ amino acids are possible; if three bases code for one amino acid, $4^3 = 64$ amino acids are possible, which will account for the 20 amino acids seen in the codon table below.

C. Universal genetic code

To resolve all the different codons, Marshall Nirenberg and J. H. Matthei made synthetic mRNAs and used them to make proteins *in vitro*. In 1961, they published their results that UUU codes for phenylalanine, AAA codes for lysine and CCC for proline. Later, Har Gobind Khorana made various possible combinations of synthetic mRNA and decoded many of the other codons. Also, there were codons for starting a polypeptide and stopping the polypeptide called *start codons* (AUG) and *stop codons* (UGA, UAG, UAA) respectively.

Some amino acids are coded by more than one codon. This multiplicity or redundancy of codons coding for one amino acid is referred to as **degeneracy**. E.g.: glycine is coded by GGG, GGA, GGU and GGC. These codons are universal from bacteria to humans with few exceptions such as paramecium, tetrahymena and mitochondria.

The universal codon table is shown below.

1st base	2nd base				3rd base
	U	C	A	G	
U	UUU - Phe UUC - Phe UUA - Leu UUG - Leu	UCU - Ser UCC - Ser UCA - Ser UCG - Ser	UAU - Tyr UAC - Tyr **UAA - Stop** **UAG - Stop**	UGU - Cys UGC - Cys **UGA - Stop** UGG - Trp	U C A G
C	CUU - Leu CUC - Leu CUA - Leu CUG - Leu	CCU - Pro CCC - Pro CCA - Pro CCG - Pro	CAU - His CAC - His CAA - Gln CAG - Gln	CGU - Arg CGC - Arg CGA - Arg CGG - Arg	U C A G
A	AUU - Ile AUC - Ile AUA - Ile **AUG - Met**	ACU - Thr ACC - Thr ACA - Thr ACG - Thr	AAU - ASN AAC - Asn AAA - Lys AAG - Lys	AGU - Ser AGC - Ser AGA - Arg AGG - Arg	U C A G
G	GUU - Val GUC - Val GUA - Val GUG - Val	GCU - Ala GCC - Ala GCA - Ala GCG - Ala	GAU - Asp GAC - Asp GAA - Glu GAG - Glu	GGU - Gly GGC - Gly GGA - Gly GGG - Gly	U C A G

Figure 15-6. Universal codon table.

D. Mutations

Mutations occurring in and around genes may affect protein synthesis, sequence and function. The different types of mutations and their effects on proteins are listed below:

- **Point mutations:** Single base pair change or substitution. Sometimes it has no effect on protein sequence or function if similar codons are substituted. E.g.: GGC to GGG still codes for Glycine. However, if the point mutation results in a different amino acid, it is called a **missense mutation.** E.g.: GGC to GAC will result in a glycine to aspartate substitution. If the change results in a stop codon, it is called **non-sense mutation.** E.g.: GGA to UGA will result in a stop instead of coding for glycine.
- **Insertions** or **deletions:** Sometimes one or more bases are inserted into or deleted from the coding sequence resulting in a **frameshift mutation** (the reading frame codons get altered). E.g.: GGC/GGA/GGC codes for glycine-glycine-glycine. If one base is deleted in this sequence, say the third base C, the reading frame now shifts to GGG/GAG/GC-, making a protein with glycine-glutamate-alanine. Similar frame shifts can hap-

pen if one or more bases are inserted. These mutations have the worst possible effects on protein sequence and function. Insertions and deletions can also happen at a chromosomal level covering large regions.

- **Inversion** or **translocation**: Sometimes, two segments of a chromosome are inverted or translocated. Inversion results in flipping the order of genes, e.g.: A-B-C becomes C-B-A, whereas translocations involve moving a part of chromosome from one place to another or to a different chromosome.

Mutations are important mechanisms in creating new genes with novel functions but may also result in less effective or non-functioning proteins with severe consequences.

Mutagenesis
Mutations may be caused by the following mechanisms:
- **Natural**: spontaneous mutations due to errors in DNA replication, repair and recombination. Some viruses can also cause mutations by interrupting the reading frame of an important gene.
- **Chemical mutagens**: base analogs (e.g. 5-bromo uracil), reactive chemicals (e.g. nitroso compounds) or intercalating chemicals (ethidium bromide).
- **Physical mutagens**: X-rays, UV rays (short wave and long wave, present in sunlight and tanning salon lights).

III. Translation

Protein synthesis occurs in the cytoplasm in eukaryotic cells. Before looking at the details of translation, let us review the different RNA molecules in translation and their functions. Almost all cellular RNA is single-stranded and forms unique secondary structures based on sequence.

RNA types and functions
1. **Transfer RNA** (tRNA) is a small (~75-80 bases) RNA folded into a clover leaf shape. It functions as an adapter between mRNA and ribosomes during protein synthesis. There are 45 different tRNAs specific for various amino acids. The amino acids are activated and then attached at the 3' region of tRNA.

    Each tRNA has an anticodon that is complementary to an mRNA codon. Since there are 64 codons and only 45 tRNAs, the third base in tRNA is sometimes inosine which can recognize A, U or C in mRNA. Inosine is a modified form of Guanine, and it does not base pair with G. This flexibility of the third base to bond with more than one codon is called **wobble**.

2. **Ribosomal RNA (rRNA)** is a major component of ribosomes and the most abundant form of RNA in cells. Approximately 60% of ribosomes are made up of rRNA and 40% are ribosomal proteins. Ribosomes are made up of small and large subunits and coordinate protein synthesis by coupling mRNA with tRNAs carrying amino acids. They also perform peptidyl transferase activity, making peptide bonds between amino acids to make proteins. The small and large subunits assemble just before

they begin protein synthesis. Ribosomes have two specific sites to bind tRNAs and perform peptide bonding. The P-site holds the tRNA carrying the growing polypeptide chain (peptidyl tRNA), and the A-site holds the tRNA carrying the next amino acid to be added (aminoacyl tRNA). The E-site (exit) is where the tRNAs leave the ribosome.

3. **Messenger RNA (mRNA)** carries the message from the gene to be translated into protein. As we saw earlier, the mRNA alone has poly(A) tail and travels to cytoplasm to be translated. mRNAs vary in length from 100 bases to 15 kilobases. The processed mRNA carry regions that are recognized by the ribosomes to start protein synthesis. In prokaryotes, the ribosome recognition site is called the Shine-Dalgarno region. In eukaryotes, the ribosome recognition site is not that well defined. However, the translation in all organisms starts with an AUG codon.

Activation of amino acids and attachment to tRNAs

Selection of a specific amino acid by attaching to the corresponding tRNA with the proper anticodon is very important for *specificity*. Since peptide bonds are thermodynamically unfavorable, amino acids must be activated and attached to the 3'-OH group of tRNA for easy transfer to the elongating polypeptide. This activation and attachment are done by aminoacyl-tRNA synthetases. There is at least one enzyme for each amino acid and its appropriate tRNA. The enzyme

1. binds to the right amino acid at its -COOH terminus and attaches an AMP by hydrolyzing an ATP;
2. recognizes the tRNA by its secondary structure and anticodon;
3. then transfers the amino acid to the 3-OH group of the correct tRNA and AMP is detached; and
4. finally releases the aminoacyl tRNA.

A. Protein synthesis

This process can be explained in three stages namely initiation, elongation and termination. The structure of ribosomes and three RNAs involved have been explained earlier.

1. Initiation

The small subunit of ribosome first recognizes the ribosome binding site (Shine-Dalgarno region in prokaryotes; the G-cap and a consensus region near the start codons in eukaryotes) at the 5' non-translated region (NTR). The first codon is almost always methionine. A special tRNA carrying a modified methionine (formyl Met) binds to the P-site. In addition, 3 initiation factors (IF), proteins that help in starting translation, and GTP bind to form initiation complex. The large subunit comes in and joins with the small subunit and rest of the initiation complex. The GTP is hydrolyzed in this step.

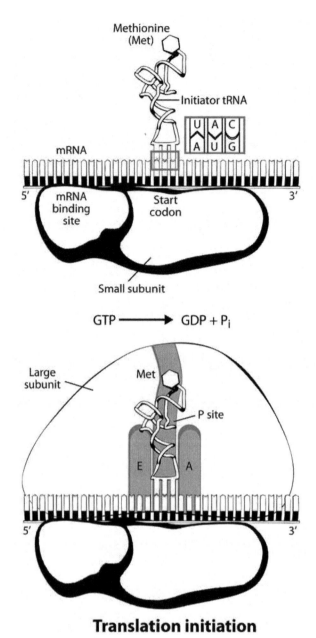

Methionine
(Met)

Initiator tRNA

U A C
A U G

mRNA

5'   3'

mRNA
binding
site

Start
codon

Small subunit

$$GTP \longrightarrow GDP + P_i$$

Large
subunit

Met

P site

E   A

5'   3'

Translation initiation

Figure 15-7. Initiation of translation

2. Elongation

The elongation of the polypeptide happens in three steps:

1. **Codon recognition:** An elongation factor (EF) helps to extend the polypeptide chain by bringing an appropriate aminoacyl tRNA (tRNA for next codon + corresponding amino acid) and places it on the A-site. A GTP attached to EF is hydrolyzed for this step.

2. **Peptide bond formation:** The peptidyl transferase activity of ribosomes transfers the first Methionine (or a growing polypeptide) from the P-site tRNA to the A-site and makes a peptide bond between the carboxyl terminus of previous amino acid and the amino terminus of incoming amino acid. The tRNA at the P-site (empty with no amino acid or protein) moves from the P-site to the E-site (exit) and leaves the ribosome.

Codon recognition

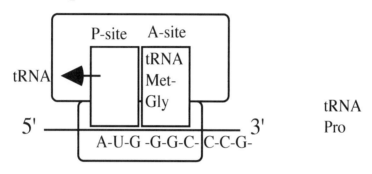

Peptide bond formation

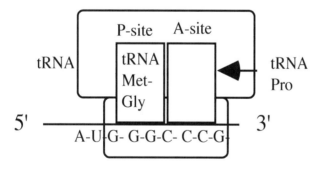

Translocation

Figure 15-8. Three steps in the elongation of polypeptide

3. **Translocation:** The t-RNA at the A-site is translocated to the P-site. Another GTP is hydrolyzed. The mRNA codons and corresponding tRNA are H-bonded. Hence when the peptidyl tRNA (tRNA with the growing polypeptide) moves from the A-site to the P-site, the mRNA also slides along. As mentioned earlier, the t-RNA that was in the P-site moves to the E-site and then leaves the ribosome. Now the next codon comes to the A-site. The elongation continues with the next codon recognition, peptide bond formation and translocation. Each elongation step takes about 60 millisecond.

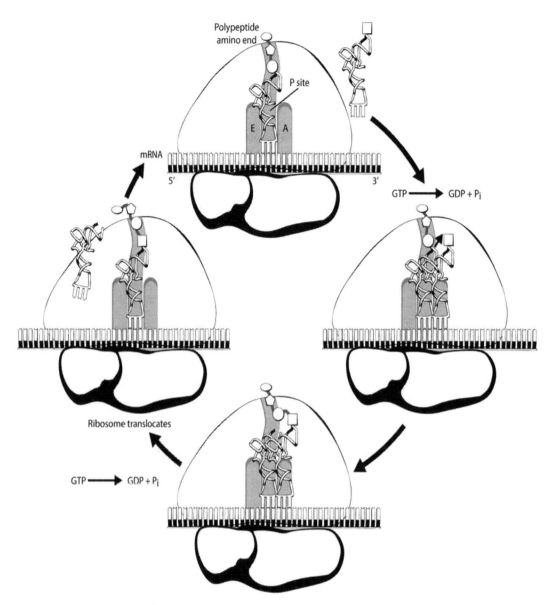

Figure 15-9. Elongation of polypeptide

3. Termination

The polypeptide elongation continues until the stop codon (termination signal: UAA, UAG or UAG) on the mRNA reaches the A-site. A **release factor** (protein) binds to this stop codon and makes peptidyl transferase add H_2O to the growing polypeptide chain. This step releases the completed polypeptide from the tRNA at the P-site and from the ribosome. The ribosome subunits separate and go on to start synthesis of a new polypeptide. One mRNA can be translated simultaneously by several ribosomes making several polypeptides continuously from one template. This combination of one mRNA and many ribosomes is called a **polysome.**

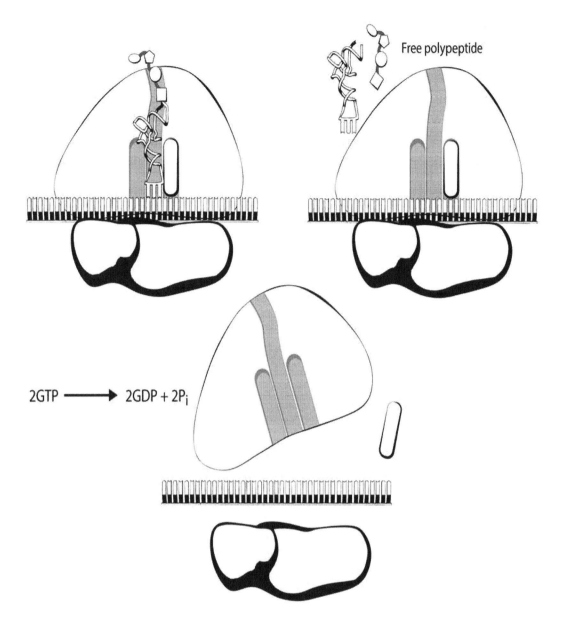

Free polypeptide

$$2GTP \longrightarrow 2GDP + 2P_i$$

Figure 15-10. Termination of polypeptide synthesis

B. Protein processing

Almost all the proteins made in eukaryotic cells undergo some form of processing before they start functioning. For example, the amino terminal is sometimes cleaved to activate the protein or to remove a target signal (a segment that tags a protein for a specific destination in a cell or for secretion). Disulfide bonds are formed between two cystines. Some amino acid side chains are chemically modified, e.g.: hydroxy proline or glycine. Glycosylation of some residues on the protein.

Summary

The DNA double helix has two major functions, namely to replicate and pass on the genetic information to next generation and to be used as template for mRNA synthesis in a highly regulated manner. The mRNA transcribed from DNA is processed in eukaryotes by adding a 5' G-cap and poly (A) tail. In prokaryotes, the mRNA is translated simultaneously. The translation occurs in cytoplasm of eukaryotes where small subunit of ribosome recognizes the 5' mRNA region starts the initiation complex. The large subunit joins and helps in making the polypeptide. The polypeptide is processed before it starts to function.

16. VIRUSES AND BACTERIA

Concepts

- Viruses are non-living obligatory parasites made up of macromolecules such as DNA/RNA and proteins with or without lipid envelope.
- Viruses are efficient in replication and are used as model systems to study molecular biology.
- Bacterial genome includes chromosomal DNA and plasmid DNA and transfer genetic material through several processes.

Outline

I. Structure and Replication of Viruses
II. Major Types of Viruses and Viral Diseases
III. Bacterial Genome and Genetics

I. Structure and Replication of Viruses

Viruses may be considered nonliving parasites because they do not have any cells, do not metabolize anything, do not make or use ATP, and do not directly reproduce their progenies without host cells.

Viruses are obligatory intracellular parasites made of genetic material and proteins. The genetic material (DNA or RNA) can program the host cells to make more viruses. The first virus identified and characterized was the Tobacco Mosaic Virus (TMV). TMV was discovered based on the following facts:

- It was transmitted from one plant to another.
- It reproduced only within the host plant.
- It could not be cultured on media.
- It could pass through bacterial filters, thus it was smaller than bacteria.
- It could not be killed by alcohol which would kill bacteria.

Wendell Stanley, an American scientist, first crystallized TMV in 1935. The crystals could be dissolved in water and be used to infect healthy tobacco plants. It was found to contain RNA and proteins only.

A. Composition of viruses

Viruses contain nucleic acids in the single-stranded or double-stranded form of DNA or RNA along with a protein capsid (coat), and they may also contain an envelope made up of viral proteins and host-derived lipids and carbohydrates. The viral DNA or RNA contains the program for the host cells to turn themselves into factories for manufacturing viruses. Viruses are classified into families based on their composition.

B. Replication of viruses:

Viruses use host machinery, such as ribosomes, enzymes, and other monomers to replicate inside the host cell. Individual viral particles are called *viri-*

ons. They have a specific host range, i.e.: they can infect a particular group of organisms and use their cells to replicate. The basic replication process includes replication of their genome (DNA or RNA) and necessary proteins, packaging the contents together inside cells, and getting released from the cells.

1. Genome replication

Viral DNA is replicated by cellular DNA polymerase (DNA-dependent DNA polymerase) using the dNTPs inside the cell. The information contained in the viral DNA programs the cell to slow down cellular metabolism and to replicate viral DNA. If the virus contains RNA, it also carries an RNA-dependent DNA polymerase enzyme, *reverse transcriptase*, which can make DNA from the RNA template. Host cells do not have reverse transcriptase. The DNA is then used to make the viral RNA by the host cell's RNA polymerase.

2. Protein synthesis

Viral proteins are made by cellular ribosomes from the mRNA transcribed from viral DNA, using cellular RNA polymerase. Once the proteins are made, they can assemble by themselves along with their genome to package new virus particles. After the assembly, the viruses may fuse with the cellular membrane and exit the cells. If the virus contains a lipid envelope, it is derived from the host's membrane during the release of the viruses. If some of the envelope proteins are coded by the viral genome, the viral proteins first get integrated into cell membrane before the virus fuses with the cell membrane with viral proteins and exits.

II. Major Types of Viruses

A. Bacteriophages

Bacteriophages or phages are viruses that infect bacteria. Lambda is one of the best studied phages. It is a circular dsDNA virus. T_2, T_4, and T_6 are called even phages. M_{13} is a filamentous phage which contains a linear ss-DNA. A bacteriophage can infect bacteria and replicate in two ways, namely through the *lytic cycle* and the *lysogenic cycle*.

1. Lytic cycle
The virus infects bacteria by introducing its genome into the host's cell and programming the bacteria to make more viruses. Once enough viruses replicate, they lyse the cell and burst out, killing the bacterium. If the bacteria are grown as a lawn (continuous colonies) and infected with a phage, small specks of lysed bacteria appear, called *plaques*.

2. Lysogenic cycle
The phage inserts its genome into the bacterial cytoplasm, where it replicates and gets integrated into the bacterial chromosome. The viral DNA injected into the chromosome it is called a **prophage**. The prophage replicates with the bacterial chromosome, and enters a latent stage, during which the virus remains dormant. Occasionally, prophages leave the chromosome and replicate independently, leading to the lytic phase.

B. Plant viruses

Some plant viruses are major pests, causing crop diseases (e.g.: TMV). In some crop plants such as rice or tomato, a virus-infected plant is severely stunted and chlorotic (yellowish). There are no chemicals to treat such infected plants, and the only solution is to isolate and burn them. Plant viruses are spread by vectors (such as insect pests), agricultural practices (**horizontal transmission**) and vegetative propagation (**vertical transmission**).

The best way to minimize plant viral diseases is to control insect pests and follow clean agricultural practices. Viruses replicate inside plants, and are transmitted within the host through phloem sap or plasmodesmata. Some plants contain **viroids**, RNA with complex secondary structures, but no coding regions. Viroids often replicate excessively and cause disease. Viroids are suspected to be escaped introns that have an ability to be replicated at a high rate, e.g.: the cadang-cadang viroid in coconut trees.

C. Animal viruses

1. Types of different animal viruses

Animal viruses are extremely diverse in their structure, infection mechanism, replication, and the diseases they cause. Some of the major viruses and the classes they belong to are listed in the table on the next page. Examples of disease-causing animal viruses in humans and animals can be grouped into categories based on their structure, genome and replication. The genome may be ssDNA, dsDNA, ssRNA, or dsRNA as shown in the Table below.

Genome	Family	Disease
dsDNA (enveloped)	Herpes virus Poxviridae	Herpes simplex I Herpes simplex II Smallpox
dsDNA (nonenveloped)	Adenovirus	Respiratory disease
ssDNA (nonenveloped)	Parvoviridae	Coinfect with adenovirus, e.g.: gasteroenteritits
dsDNA (nonenveloped)	Reoviridae	Diarrhea

ssRNA (enveloped)
  serve as mRNA (+)
  template for mRNA (-)
	Filoviridae
	Orthomyxoviridae
		Ebola
		Influenza

ssRNA (+) with DNA step in replication	Retroviridae	HIV Leukemia
ssRNA (nonenveloped)	Picornaviridae	Common cold Measles Mumps Polio

These viruses may or may not have a host-derived envelope. Some RNA viruses contain a + strand of RNA that serves as mRNA and as a template for the - strand RNA replication. Some contain a - strand of RNA that serves as the template for both mRNA synthesis and + RNA replication. Some viruses, such as retroviruses, contain RNA that is converted into DNA by reverse transcriptases, which are carried within viruses; the DNA is then used as a template for RNA synthesis and replication.

2. Replication of animal viruses

Depending on the viral type, replication is done either through the productive cycle or through both the reproductive and latent cycles. This is similar to the lytic and lysogenic cycles of bacteriophages. In the **productive cycle**, viral genomes are replicated, proteins are synthesized, and they self-assemble together into virions and exit the cell. The cells may lyse or continue to make more viruses. E.g.: cold virus, measles, and mumps viruses. Enveloped viruses assemble inside the cell, fuse with the cell membrane and exit the cells with the lipid bilayer of the host embedded with some viral proteins and some host proteins. E.g.: small pox, influenza and Ebola viruses.

In the **latent cycle**, the virus infects and replicates its genome, and is integrated into host chromosomes, thereafter replicating along with the cellular DNA. The integrated virus is called a **provirus**, and it remains latent for a considerable amount of time. Proteins may be produced from the viral genome, but replication is limited. At some stage, the provirus gets activated, the viral replication becomes rapid and independent of cellular DNA. The disease symptoms become acute after this stage. This pathway is followed by some DNA viruses such as the herpes virus and almost all retroviruses such as human immunodeficiency virus (HIV) and human T-cell leukemia virus (HTLV).

3. Example: Human Immunodeficiency Virus (HIV) and AIDS

HIV is a retrovirus containing two ssRNA molecules and two reverse transcriptase enzymes enclosed in a lipid envelope with glycoproteins coded by HIV and the host cell. HIV fuses with the host cell's plasma membrane by binding to a specific receptor protein, CD4, recognized by its gp120 protein. Once fused, the proteins in the capsid are degraded by enzymes (such as serine proteases), and the viral genome is released into cells. The viral enzyme reverse transcriptase makes a complementary DNA (cDNA) strand from the RNA template. The cellular DNA polymerase makes dsDNA from the cDNA and the dsDNA is integrated into the cell's chromosome by the HIV's enzyme, integrase. HIV proteins are made during the latent stage and disease symptoms may not be fully obvious. The latent stage can be as long as 10 years. In some people the disease never shows up for some unknown reason. However, in most cases, the HIV replicates rapidly after the latent stage and AIDS symptoms show up. Since the HIV's reverse transcriptase has a higher error rate than the cellular DNA polymerases, there is a high rate of mutations in HIV allowing it to evolve quickly and become resistant to drugs.

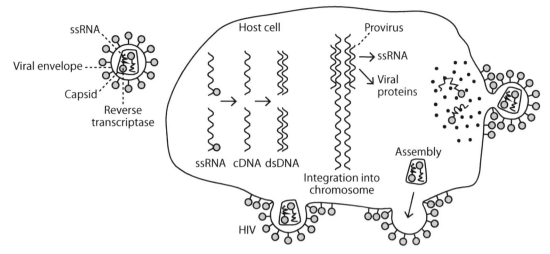

Labels in figure:
ssRNA
Viral envelope
Capsid
Reverse transcriptase
Host cell
ssRNA cDNA dsDNA
Integration into chromosome
HIV
Provirus
ssRNA
Viral proteins
Assembly

Figure 16-1. Replication of HIV in human cell

D. Treatment of viral diseases:

Treatment of viral diseases is difficult due to the nature of viruses and their mechanism of infection and replication. Many disease-causing viruses mutate and reproduce so fast that they rapidly develop resistance to drugs. So combination drug therapies are used to mitigate the problem. Viral DNA replicates using the host's machinery. So any drugs used to control viral replication inhibit cellular metabolism with severe side effects. The immune system is the best defense so far, but sometimes the immune system is tricked by the viral envelope having host membrane proteins, and some viruses, like HIV, attack the immune system itself.

Drugs and treatments available for viral diseases
- **Vaccines:** Effective against slow-evolving viruses like small pox, polio, rubella, measles and mumps. Not effective for fast-evolving viruses.
- **Antiviral drugs:** Some examples of drugs that have been effective against some viral replication mechanisms are given below:
  - Acyclovir, used to treat herpes infection, is a nucleotide analog that inhibits DNA synthesis.
  - Amantadine is used to treat influenza type A by inhibiting the uncoating of the protein.
  - AZT (Zidovudine) is also a nucleotide analog used to inhibit HIV replication with severe side effects because it blocks cellular replication.
  - Serine protease inhibitors are newly-developed drugs to treat HIV patients. This drug inhibits the uncoating of HIV inside the cell. E.g., Saquinavir is one of the first approved drugs in this class.

The current approaches to finding a treatment for HIV and AIDS include vaccines created using the viral glycoprotein gp120 and the development of drugs to inhibit reverse transcriptase. Also, scientists are studying individuals who seem to have a natural immunity to AIDS and are trying combination therapies to minimize the effects of the disease. Major problems in making progress include the impact of treatments on the immune system, the high mutation rate of HIV proteins and the severe side effects of the drugs being tried.

III. Bacterial Genome and Genetics

Bacteria and viruses have been excellent model systems to study molecular genetics because of their simple and small genome, rapid multiplication in a short time period, and the large genetic variations that occur within a selected population.

A. The bacterial genome

The bacterial genome includes chromosomal DNA and episomes, which are extrachromosomal DNA present as plasmid(s).

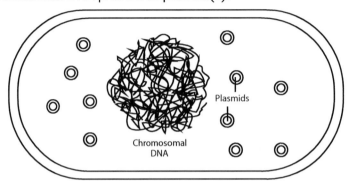

Figure 16-2. Chromosomal and plasmid DNA in bacteria

1. Chromosomes

Bacterial chromosomes are approximately 4,000 to 5,000 kb with about 3,000 genes. The chromosome contains a single origin of replication and they replicate once in 20 minutes prior to each cell division. Chromosomes also contain some extrachromosomal DNA from plasmids and viral DNAs that have been integrated into them.

2. Plasmid DNA

Plasmids are extrachromosomal circular DNA molecules. Plasmids vary in size, the genes they carry, and their functions. They contain a single origin of replication and replicate independently of the chromosome. They are divided among the daughter cells randomly during binary fission, or are specifically transmitted to other cells by different mechanisms.

- **F-plasmid** (Fertility factor): It is approximately 93 kb in length and contains genes that confer "maleness," and code for an F-pili. It is transmitted through sexual mating. The F-plasmid is sometimes present as a part of the chromosome. When it excises from the chromosome it may carry a few more genes, becoming as long as 100 kb or more, now called an **F'** plasmid or episome.
- **R-plasmid** (Resistance factor): This includes a wide range of extrachromosomal DNA, varying in size from 3 to 117 kb, that carry genes for antibiotic resistance.
- **Colicinogenic factors:** These plasmids, varying in size from 4 to 141 kb, carry genes coding for toxins (colicin). The R-plasmids and C-factors are important for the survival of bacteria. These may also carry some genes for sexual mating.

3. Transposable elements (transposons)

Transposons are mobile genetic elements, or "jumping genes," which can transpose from one part of a chromosome to another part or a different chromosome. These were first characterized in maize by Barbara McClintock and later they were found to be present in bacteria and other organisms. The different types of transposons in bacteria are listed below:

- **Insertion sequences** (IS) are simple transposons varying in size from 768 (IS1) to about 1537 (IS50R) bases. They contain inverted repeats at their terminals and carry enzymes called transposases to move from one place to another in the chromosome.
- **Complex transposons** contain inverted repeats at their terminals in addition to the antibiotic resistance genes they carry. They are also longer, varying from 3100 (Tn903; kanamycin resistance) to 9300 (Tn10; tetracycline resistance) base pairs in length.

These transposable elements recognize a specific DNA sequence in the target region (the site they are moving into), cut the DNA and insert themselves using the enzyme transposase. These elements are critical in generating new combinations of genes, mutations and ultimately the microevolution of bacteria to survive challenging environments.

B. Transfer and recombination of bacterial DNA:

Bacterial DNA is introduced from one bacterium to another by conjugation, transduction or transformation.

1. Conjugation

The sexual mating of bacteria through F-pili (plural; pilus = singular), conjugation allows the genes present in the F-factor to be transferred from an F^+ bacteria to an F^- bacteria. Bacterial conjugation was discovered by Lederberg and Tatum in 1946 when they were analyzing bacterial mutants (see later) which transferred genes necessary for certain amino acid biosynthesis through F-pili. The F-factor is transmitted as a single strand from one bacterium into another bacterium through the F-pilus.

After the transfer, it is converted into dsDNA, and it may exist as an F^- episome or be integrated into the chromosome (as an F-factor). When it is integrated into the chromosome, the bacteria is referred to as a high frequency recombination (hfr) strain. If it exists as an F-episome in bacteria already containing an F-factor in the chromosome, the genes present in these two are allelic to each other, and they can recombine, resulting in new genotypes.

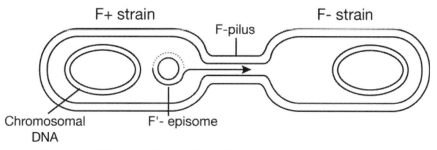

Figure 16-3. Transfer of F-plasmid by conjugation

The F-factor in chromosomes of an hfr strain sometimes separate from the chromosome and get transferred to an F- bacteria. This process is also referred to as sexduction.

2. Transduction

Transfer of a part of a chromosome from one bacterium to another, mediated through a phage, is referred to as **transduction**. The transduction may be general, wherein random fragments from bacterial chromosomes are transmitted by phages or specific, in which certain sequences are always carried by phages from one strain to another. Transduction is also referred to as *transfection*, which is an experimental method used to introduce DNA fragments into bacteria using phages as vectors (to carry the DNA and replicate in a bacteria). Transfection is an efficient method to transform bacteria, express foreign genes in bacteria and, for DNA library construction, which are explained in a later chapter.

3. Transformation

Introduction of DNA from an external medium into the bacteria. You may recall Fredrick Griffith's experiment followed by the experiment of Avery et al., showing that bacteria isolated from a S-strain can be used to transform the R-strain. Salt solutions, heat shock, freezing and thawing, and electroporation are some of the methods used to transform bacterial cells.

17. REGULATION OF GENE EXPRESSION

Concepts

- Genes are regulated by proteins that bind to regulatory sequences that are upstream or downstream of the transcribed sequences.
- Prokaryotic genes are organized in units called operons and they are regulated by metabolites binding to proteins that recognize and bind to operators.
- Eukaryotes have complex mechanisms for the regulation of gene expression due to their multicellular nature and complex functions.
- Regulation of gene expression in eukaryotes occurs at multiple levels such as transcriptional, post-transcriptional, translational and post-translational.

Outline

I. Regulation of Gene Expression in Prokaryotes

Gene expression refers to the synthesis of RNA from a DNA template. The RNA may code for mRNA, rRNA, or tRNA. Broadly speaking, gene expression also includes the translation of mRNA(s) into specific protein(s) resulting in specific phenotype(s). Gene expression may be constitutive or regulated. Constitutive genes are expressed continuously without much regulation, such as genes vital for the routine functioning of the organism. However, some genes are expressed in a tightly regulated manner. It is important to understand the structure of bacterial genes to understand their regulation.

Bacterial genes are organized into units called operons. An operon constitutes the coding sequences of the genes in that unit, a promoter, and an operator. The promoter and operator determine the accuracy and amount of transcription respectively.

The DNA sequence of the promoter alone can alter the level of gene transcripts. As we saw earlier, bacterial RNA is polycistronic, i.e.: many transcripts are made from one operon simultaneously as a single mRNA in a single transcription. This is an efficient way of controlling the transcription process. The operator serves as the on-off switch to regulate the transcription in response to environmental stimuli. The operons may be either induced (inducible or positive regulation) or repressed (negative regulation).

A. Inducible operon

Inducible operons are mostly turned off, and they are turned on only when necessary, e.g.: lac operon. The lac operon is induced under two situations—namely when lactose is present with glucose or alone. When lactose is present along with glucose, the cells prefer glucose. However, the expression of genes for lactose-utilizing enzymes is activated by removing a repressor that is bound to the operator of the lac operon. The lactose binds to the repressor molecule, and the operon is derepressed to start transcription.

Further activation: If there is no glucose and only lactose is present, it results in an increase of cyclicAMP (cAMP) levels in the cells. The cAMP binds to a catabolite activator protein (CAP) and that binds to the promoter to further enhance the activity of the lac operon above the basal level created from de-repression alone.

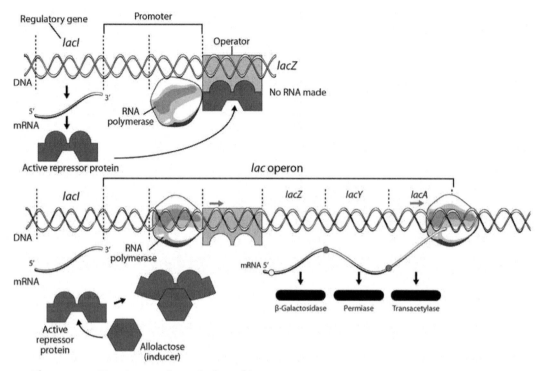

Figure 17-1. Structure and regulation of lac operon

Inducible operons are normally present to control catabolic pathways used to break down compounds.

B. Repressible operon
These are used for anabolic pathways to synthesize compounds. Repressible operons are mostly turned on, and they are turned off when not needed, e.g.: trp-operon to synthesize tryptophan. The enzymes in the trp biosynthetic pathway are expressed only when trp is absent. When trp is absent, a repressor protein is inactive and does not bind to the operator to repress transcription. When sufficient levels of trp are made, it binds to the repressor molecule and makes it an active repressor that now binds to the operator and stops transcription. This is similar to the feedback inhibition of enzymes except that it occurs at the gene level. Trp acts as a corepressor and controls the transcription of genes in its operon.

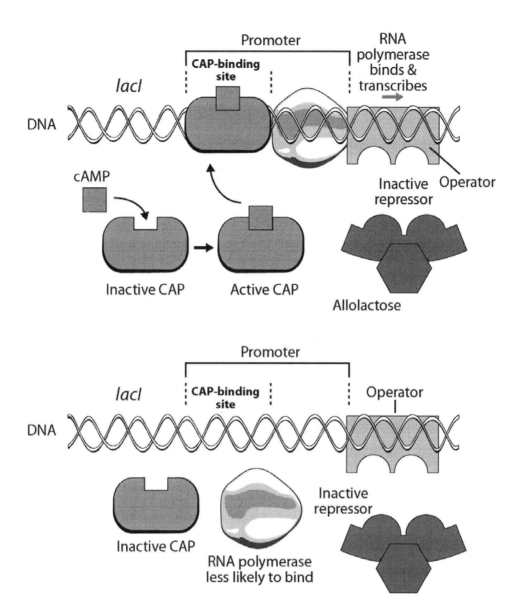

Figure 17-2. Regulation of lac operon in the presence and absence of cAMP

The regulation of the Trp operon is shown in Figure 17-3.

Gene regulation is also controlled by other proteins such as sigma factors, which can bind to the regulatory elements of bacteria and activate transcription. There are several types of sigma factors and other DNA-binding proteins that regulate prokaryotic gene expression. Such factors can transmit environmental signals to the genes to express the needed proteins immediately in response to the stimulus.

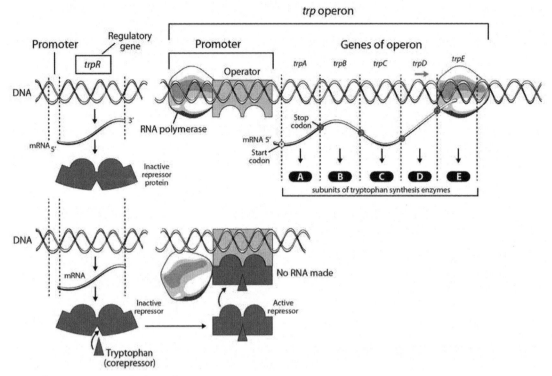

Figure 17-3. Regulation of trp operon

11. Eukaryotic Genome Structure and Genes

A. Genome size

The chromosomal DNA inside the nucleus is dispersed as chromatin during most of the cell cycle. The double helix of DNA wraps around histone proteins to form nucleosomes, which condense further to make chromatin as explained in Chapter 9. Eukaryotic chromosomes are linear molecules with defined ends called *telomeres*. The amount of DNA and number of chromosomes varies greatly among eukaryotes, so does the DNA length and number of genes. A rough idea about the number of genes in eukaryotes vs. prokaryotes might suggest a general trend of increasing size with the increasing complexities of genomes. However, genome size is not necessarily a representation of organismal complexity. For example, humans contain 46 chromosomes, whereas some crabs contain as many as 200 and some ferns up to 1,000. It is the sequence of DNA and the proteins coded by them, and not the amount of DNA alone, that determines how complex a species is. Much of the apparently excessive DNA is made of repetitive sequences that generally do not code for proteins.

B. Repetitive DNA

Most of the DNA in eukaryotic genomes, in contrast to prokaryotic genomes, is made of DNA sequences that do not code for any RNA or protein. About 10% to 25% of higher eukaryotic DNA is made up of repetitive DNA with 5 to 10 bases repeated 1,000s of times. Such repetitive DNA can be identified by reannealing denatured DNA. As we saw in the structure of the DNA double helix, dsDNA can be denatured and renatured by heating and cooling. When the strands renature, complementary sequences base pair to anneal. Based on how fast DNA reanneals, one can determine if it consists of highly repetitive or unique sequences. Based on such studies and others (explained in Chapter 15), unique sequences or single copy genes can be detected. Repetitive sequences are found near telomeres and are useful in the DNA replication process because they fold onto themselves to provide a 3'-OH group for DNA synthesis.

C. Multiple gene families

Some genes are present in a single copy or a few copies, whereas some other genes are present in large numbers and are organized into *gene families*. This is the result of gene duplication during crossing over, or a result of transposable elements translocating a gene from one chromosome to another, or to a different location on the same chromosome. Genes essential for the survival of an organism are highly duplicated during evolution. Such duplicated copies of genes may mutate and evolve independently. Sometimes, they lose their regulatory sequences (promoter and other cis-elements) and are not expressed at all. Such genes are called **pseudogenes**. The multigene family members may be located together on a chromosome, or spread out in different chromosomes. Such families can be detected by DNA-DNA hybridization techniques explained in the next chapter. The expression of multigene family members is regulated by common cis-acting elements recognized by common trans-acting factors specific for that gene family. This is referred to as **coordinated gene expression**. Globin genes coding for the subunits of hemoglobin are an example of a multigene family.

III. Regulation of Gene Expression in Eukaryotes

Eukaryotic genes are organized differently from those of prokaryotes. The messages of eukaryotic genes are *monocistronic* (one mRNA per transcription to make one protein), and many genes contain intervening sequences (introns) that must be removed and exons that must be spliced together. Additionally, processed mRNA contains a 5' G-cap and 3' poly (A) tail. Similar to prokaryotes, there are some genes expressed constantly (constitutive genes) and some are highly regulated in their expression. Eukaryotic genes are regulated by a set of regulatory DNA sequences (collectively known as cis-acting elements), which are recognized by trans-acting factors. This concept was introduced in an earlier chapter. Here, we will see how eukaryotic gene expression is regulated at various levels. In prokaryotes, transcription and translation can occur simultaneously, for there is no nucleus to separate transcription from translation and no introns to be removed. In eukaryotes, gene expression can be regulated at the transcriptional level, posttranscriptional level, translational level, or posttranslational level.

A. Transcriptional regulation

The rate of transcription is regulated at the gene level with different mechanisms operating for long-term and short-term controls.

1. Long-term transcriptional control
Chromosomes are condensed during cell division, but gradually uncoil again to become dispersed as chromatin. However, a portion of chromatin re-

mains condensed as **heterochromatin**, which is not readily accessible by RNA polymerases and other proteins. Some regions are more diffuse, existing as **euchromatin,** and are accessible for transcription. E.g.: one of the X-chromosomes in females is inactivated and such condensed chromosomes are called **Barr bodies**.

Another way to control transcription on selected chromosomes is to methylate the DNA. **Methylation** is done by **DNA methylases** such as deoxy cytosine methylase (DCM) or deoxy adenosine methylase (DAM) which add methyl groups to the C and A bases respectively. DNA methylation at the C and A nucleotides results in the prevention of such regions from being transcribed. In humans as much as 5% of DNA is methylated and only about 3% to 5% of genes are actively transcribed at any given time. DNA methylation also helps DNA polymerase to distinguish the old strand from the new strand. In bacteria, DNA methylation is critical for recognizing cellular versus viral DNA. The pattern and amount of methylation varies with species.

2. Short-term transcriptional control
Some regions of chromosomes are actively transcribed as **transcription puffs.** Such regions can be easily seen in the large multistranded polytene chromosomes in the salivary gland cells of Drosophila larva. Transcription of genes in eukaryotes is controlled by the interaction between transcription factors and the regulatory elements on the genes. The regulatory elements include the promoter, which is closer to and upstream of the start site, and enhancers or repressors, which may be upstream or downstream from the start site. The promoter is present at a relatively fixed distance, whereas other elements may be present close to or far from the start site.

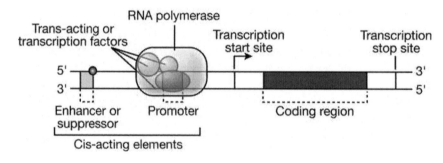

Figure 17-4. Structure of an eukaryotic gene

The trans-acting proteins recognize specific cis-acting elements on the DNA by binding to a specific DNA base sequence and inducing or inhibiting transcription. Some factors directly bind to RNA polymerase or other DNA binding proteins, and affect transcription through protein-protein interaction. Transcription factors have unique secondary structures to recognize the DNA, and can be grouped into the following categories:
- **Helix-turn-helix proteins**: These proteins contain alpha-helix, beta-turn, and alpha-helix secondary structures that fit within the grooves of DNA. The protein sequences can vary and thus bind to different DNA sequences.
- **Zinc finger proteins**: These proteins contain zinc ions covalently bonded to certain residues, which protrude as fingers and recognize DNA.
- **Leucine zippers**: These proteins contain multiple leucine residues, which

interact because of the hydrophobic nature of their side chains.

All these DNA binding proteins act as dimers, which interact with each other along these motifs (unique secondary/tertiary strictures) and with DNA to regulate transcription.

Some hormones can bind to these transcription factors in cytoplasm and then migrate to the nucleus, bind with specific cis-acting elements, and activate the transcription of certain genes. This is one mechanism by which hormones secreted by the glands travel to other cells, bind to specific receptors, enter the cells, interact with transcription factors and activate genes.

B. Post-transcriptional regulation

This type of regulation is limited compared to transcriptional regulation. Post-transcriptional regulation involves differential processing of the mRNA transcript or relative stabilities of mRNA.

- **Alternate splicing:** This happens during mRNA processing, wherein introns are removed and exons spliced. Some mRNAs are processed differently to yield different proteins. For example, exons 1, 2, and 3 may be joined to form one kind of protein and exons 1 and 3 alone joined to make another kind of protein.
- **mRNA stability:** On the other hand, some mRNAs have unique sequences at the 5' or 3' NTRs that affect their stability in the cytoplasm. Some mRNAs are long-lived, for up to several days, and some are short-lived, lasting only a few minutes after transcription. When mRNAs are long-lived, it allows the translation to continue for a longer time. The mRNA stability is altered by RNA binding proteins which may tag the mRNA for degradation or degrade the mRNA themselves.

C. Translational regulation

Translation in eukaryotes occurs in the cytoplasm and involves several proteins known as initiation factors and elongation factors. Also, depending on the sequence of the ribosome recognition site on the mRNA, mRNA can be translated more efficiently or less efficiently. Another translational control is to block translation of processed mRNA until the need arises.

Examples of translational regulation are given below:

- **mRNA storage:** Many processed mRNAs are stored in the nucleus of an egg prior to fertilization and are translated after fertilization and during embryonic development. This control may be exerted by not modifying the 5' G-cap or not having the right initiation factor present until the cells are ready to translate such mRNAs.
- **Hormonal regulation:** An alternate mechanism involves hormonal action. For example, the casein mRNA is translated 25 times more efficiently in the presence of the hormone prolactin to produce the milk protein casein. Prolactin is made when the animal is ready for lactation.
- **Cofactor influence:** Another example of translational control via cofactors is the synthesis and assembly of globins and hemes to make hemoglobin. Hemoglobins consist of two α-globins, two β-globins, and 4 small heme molecules (cofactors). When heme molecules accumulate, they increase the translational efficiency of globin mRNAs.

D. Post-translational modification

This is the last stage of controlling gene expression at the protein level. Some examples of post-translational modifications or processing of proteins were discussed in an earlier Chapter on protein synthesis and processing. Post-translational processing results in functional proteins in most situations automatically. However, in some situations it is used as a regulatory mechanism. Examples of such regulation include the following:

- **Zymogen activation:** Some proteins are first made in inactive forms and later they are converted to active forms. For example, insulin is first made as proinsulin, and then it is converted to insulin to become active.
- **Selective targeting:** For membrane proteins and proteins targeted for specific organelles to be active, they should be in the right place. A segment of proteins, normally at the NH_2-terminal, determines the protein's target site. The protein may then be transported through Golgi vesicles to the right membrane or organelle. Once it reaches its destination, the target peptide (also called the leader sequence or signal sequence) is removed and the protein becomes active. Sometimes if the protein does not reach the target, often because of defective target signaling, the protein remains in the cytoplasm and is degraded. E.g.: the chloride channel protein in cystic fibrosis is mutated and does not reach the target.
- **Chemical modification:** Phosphorylation can make proteins active or inactive. In the cell cycle, cyclin levels are modulated by phosphorylation and the activation of proteases that will degrade cyclin. In the Na^+/K^+ pump, the transport of Na^+ out and K^+ in is facilitated by phosphorylation and dephosphorylation. Phosphorylation happens at the -OH group of serine, threonine, and tyrosine.
- **Glycoslylation:** Many membrane proteins are glycosylated after translation in the Golgi apparatus or rough ER. Short oligosaccharides are added to serine or threonine at their -OH group (O-linked glycosylation) or to asparagine at the $-NH_2$ group (N-linked glycosylation). Glycosylation reduces degradation by proteases and facilitates signal transduction.

IV. Gene Regulation and Development

The program for the development of an organism is encoded in genes. All multicellular organisms start as a single cell: a zygote in sexual reproduction or an embryonic cell in asexual reproduction. The single cell having the potential to become a whole new organism is called **totipotency**. Totipotency is observed in several types of cells in plants, whereas it is mainly in the zygotic cells of animals. Totipotent cells undergo division, differentiation, and growth to become a fully developed organism with different types of cells, tissues and organs. The interplay of genes, proteins, internal chemical signals, such as hormones, and the external environment in this developmental process is complex, and we are only beginning to understand such processes in higher animals. It is beyond the scope of this book to cover developmental processes of multicellular organisms. However, these examples of changes at the genetic level give some idea as to how the developmental process may be regulated.

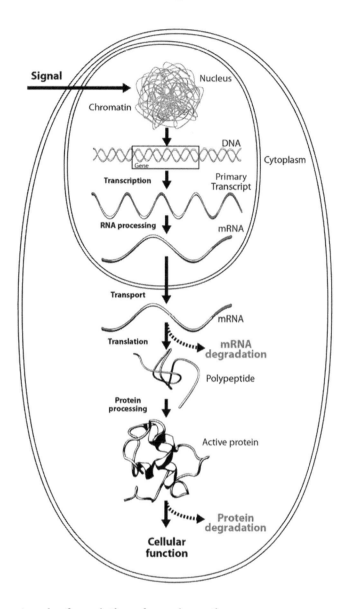

Figure 17-5. Levels of regulation of an eukaryotic gene

A. Genomic rearrangement

As cells divide and develop, some genes are rearranged to express certain genes in a variable manner. For example, immunoglobulin (antibody) genes coding for four different peptides can rearrange themselves to shuffle their genes in order to create a wide diversity of the proteins resulting from them. Another example of gene rearrangement is in the yeast mating type involving a- and α-types, which can be reshuffled to create new mating types in alternate generations. If the arrangement is α-α-a, it results in the α type and if the a-gene is copied and used to replace the middle of a gene, it becomes α-a-a and results in the a-type.

- **Transposable elements**: Transposable elements provide the opportunity for various genes to be moved from one place to another (see Chapter 16). Transposable elements in eukaryotes vary from prokaryotic transposons in that they do not exist independently, but move with RNA as an intermediate and lack antibiotic genes. These elements can be integrated randomly or in hot spots of chromosomes. Sometimes, genes are interrupted and inactivated by transposable elements. The details of their transposition and their roles in eukaryotes are not well known. One reason suggested for their existence is to create variation among the gene pool so that organisms can adapt to varying environments.
- **Master genes controlling development**: Certain genes, **homeotic genes**, control a wide array of other genes involved in development. They were first characterized in Drosophila in which mutants of altered physical traits, such as antenna in place of eyes, were isolated. These master genes or homoeotic genes mostly code for transcription factors that can bind to a common regulatory sequence on several genes involved in the developmental process.
- **Gene Amplification**: Sometimes certain genes are duplicated several times to amplify their number, so that enough copies of mRNAs can be produced. The genes for ribosomal RNA are amplified at earlier stages of development so that there are enough copies of rRNA genes to make rRNA for ribosomes and mRNA for ribosomal proteins. In some cases, the genes for herbicide resistance are amplified to survive the chemical.

B. Tissue-specific gene expression

During and after development, genes are expressed in a tissue-specific manner to facilitate the function of different cell or tissue types. For example, leaf tissues in a plant will make proteins for photosynthesis, and storage tissues in the seed will make storage proteins. This tissue specific expression of genes is controlled by the transcription factors being selectively active in specific tissues.

C. Coordinated gene expression

Multiple genes in a biochemical pathway may be located in different loci of a same chromosomes or sometimes in different chromosomes. All of them need to be ex pressed in a coordinated manner by having a similar regulatory sequences recognized by a common transcription factor.

18. RECOMBINANT DNA TECHNOLOGY

Concepts

- Recombinant DNA technology allows genes conferring specific traits to be transferred from one organism to another without species barrier.
- Applications of recombinant DNA span from agriculture to modern medicine and forensics.

Outline

I.   Basic Tools and Techniques
II. Gene Isolation, Characterization and Transfer
III. Application of Genetic Engineering to Humans, Animals, and Agriculture
IV. Bioethics and Safety Issues

1. Basic Tools and Techniques

Recombinant DNA technology is based on the central dogma of molecular biology that DNA makes RNA makes protein and the fact that if you modify the gene you can modify the protein. Recombinant DNA techniques are used to study molecular aspects of life and to apply the information in a constructive and ethical manner to benefit life through academic and commercial research. Recombinant DNA technology refers to a set of techniques used to isolate, recombine, transfer and express genes or DNA for further study. Like any other technology, recombinant DNA work is dependent on certain basic tools such as enzymes and plasmids, and certain techniques are essential. A selected list of such tools and techniques are briefly described below.

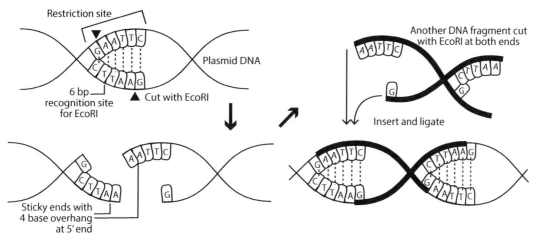

Figure 18-1. Restriction digestion and ligation to make recombinant DNA

A. Common enzymes used in molecular biology

1. **Restriction endonucleases:** enzymes isolated from prokaryotes that recognize a specific DNA sequence and cleave the DNA at that recognition site or another place. Different types of restriction endonucleases

protect cells from invading viruses and foreign DNA. Some are generic, i.e.: cut DNA nonspecifically, and some are specific. Among the specific restriction enzymes, type I and type III recognize at one site and cleave at another place. Additionally, type I and III have methylase activity. Type II are the most commonly used enzymes without methylase activity, and they recognize and cleave at a particular DNA sequence. The enzymes are named after the bacterium they are isolated from, e.g.: EcoRI, from *E. coli*, can recognize and cut DNA with the sequence 5'-GAATTC-3', a six base pair recognition enzyme. Other enzymes recognize four base pairs or longer. Once the enzyme cuts the DNA, they may leave an overhang of four base pairs at the 5' or 3' end or they may leave a blunt end. The 5' or 3' overhangs are called **sticky ends**, because they can anneal with similar sticky ends based on their complementarity. These enzymes are used to create recombinant DNA molecules.

2. **DNA polymerase:** used to make DNA *in vitro*. DNA synthesis is accomplished by providing a DNA template, suitable primers (oligonucleotides, 15 to 30 base long, DNA primer complementary to template), dNTPs, a DNA polymerase, Mg^{++}, and a suitable buffer with the optimum pH and ionic condition. Commonly used DNA polymerases are obtained from *E. coli*, T_7 bacteriophage, or thermostable bacteria, and are used for various applications, such as DNA synthesis, DNA sequencing, and polymerase chain reactions.

3. **DNA ligase**: As we saw in DNA replication, DNA ligase can catalyze the covalent bonding of the 3' and 5' ends of two DNA strands. This is used to connect two DNA strands having blunt ends or complementary sticky ends created by restriction enzymes to make a recombinant DNA molecule. E.g.: T4 DNA ligase obtained from the T4 phage is one the most commonly used ligases.

4. **Reverse transcriptase** (RT): Reverse transcriptase is an RNA-dependent DNA polymerase, i.e. it uses an RNA template to make a complementary DNA (**cDNA**). This is used in cDNA library construction and to amplify DNA from RNA. The commonly used RTs are isolated from viruses such as AMV (an avian virus) and MMLV (a murine virus). Some thermostable DNA polymerases also have reverse transcriptase activity under different salt conditions.

B. Vectors and hosts:

Vectors are the DNA vehicles that can carry genes from one organism to another, and allow it to replicate in a particular host. *E. coli* is one of the most commonly used host systems in recombinant DNA. Others include yeast, plant cells, and animal cells maintained in cell cultures. Some commonly used vectors are plasmid- or phage-based.

Plasmid vectors

Cloning refers to the process of making multiple identical copies of a particular DNA fragment or a gene after making the recombinant DNA and introducing it into a suitable bacterial host (transformation). Plasmid vectors are used to clone genes of relatively small size (100 bp to 15 kbp) and they are relatively less efficient than phage vectors. However, plasmid vectors are easier to handle and are more stable to maintain than phage vectors. E.g. pBluescript is one of the commonly used plasmid vector.

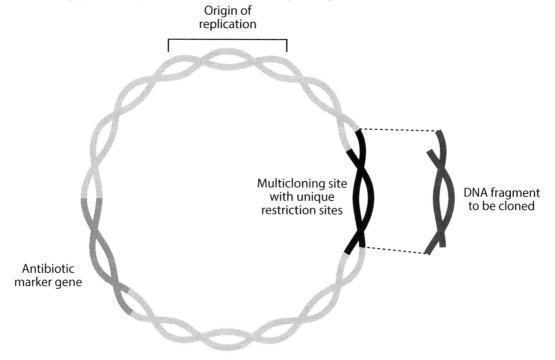

Figure 18-2. Cloning vector

2. **Phage vectors:** These are derived from lambda phage, a small phage (approximately 48 kbp) that can accommodate DNA fragments of 10 to 20 kbp in a region that is nonessential.

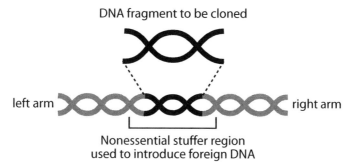

Figure 18-3. Phage vector

The nonessential region in the middle of the phage is removed and foreign DNA is inserted. Then the phage is used to infect the *E. coli* host (transfection) to introduce the gene and to multiply it. This **transfection** is more efficient than transformation.

The Figure 18.4 illustrates the prcess of cloing a gene coding of green florescent protein (GFP) from jelly fish by using a plasmid vector from *E. coli* and reintroducing the recombinant DNA into *E. coli* to replicate the cloned GFP gene.

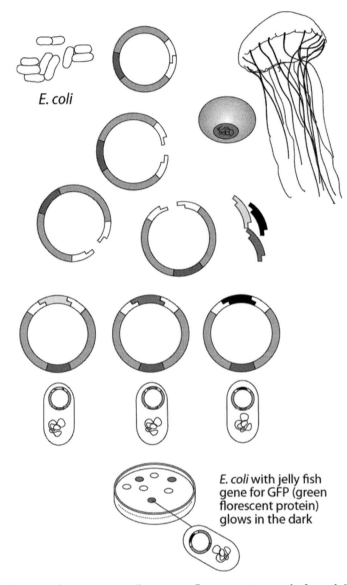

Figure 18-4. Cloning of a gene encoding green flourescent protein from jelly fish

C. Basic techniques:

A. Gel electrophoresis

This is used to fractionate DNA or RNA fragments based on their size. The negative charges on the DNA or RNA make them migrate toward the anode (+) through tiny pores in agarose or polyacrylamide gel. The molecules migrate depending on their size and the electric voltage in the system. Larger molecules move slowly and smaller molecules move quickly. The higher the voltage, the faster they move. Agarose gels are used to fractionate DNA or RNA. These are easier to make, but the size fractionation is approximate. Polyacrylamide gels are used to fractionate proteins and DNA. Polyacrylamide gels are relatively harder to make but provide better resolution of size. The accuracy of polyacrylamide gels varies from approximate fraction-ation of proteins to accurate separation of DNA in DNA-sequencing gels depending upon the thickness, length and the size of the molecules being separated.

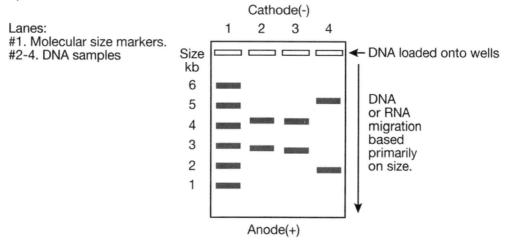

Figure 18-5. Gel electrophoresis of DNA

B. Restriction fragment length polymorphism (RFLP)

This is a technique commonly used to identify differences in the restriction pattern of a specific gene or DNA region between several individuals of a species or several related species. The DNA is cut by selected restriction en-zymes and fractionated on an agarose gel. The differences in the sizes of the fragments obtained from the restriction digestion are used to identify the relationship between individuals. For example, samples 1 and 2 (in lanes 2 and 3) in the above figure show identical restriction patterns but sample 3 (in lane 4) is different. It shows that sample 3 is from a similar gene which has a mutation in the restriction sites used to cut the DNA. This procedure is also referred to as **DNA finger printing**.

C. Radiolabeling DNA fragments

To identify a DNA fragment in an organism, it is important to label DNA with a radioisotope or fluorescent label that can be detected using X-ray film.

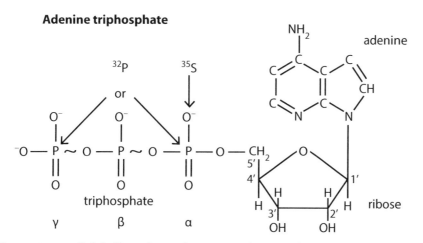

Figure 18-6. Radiolabeling of DNA fragment using a radio nucleotide

The most commonly used isotopes are ^{35}S or ^{32}P to label DNA or RNA. These isotopes are used in reactions to synthesize DNA or RNA and are incorporated into the strands during such synthesis. The following diagram shows the locations of such labels. The ^{32}P is incorporated either in the alpha position or gamma position depending on the purpose. Radiolabeling is used in DNA sequencing, Southern and Northern techniques, as explained below.

D. DNA Sequencing

The dideoxy chain termination method was originally developed by Sanger. DNA sequencing is done by doing an *in vitro* DNA synthesis using a DNA template, a specific primer, dNTPs and DNA polymerase to extend the new strand of DNA from the primer in a suitable buffer. The sequence of the complementary strand is obtained by stopping the chain extension by randomly incorporating dideoxynucleotides labeled with fluorescent molecules. Each of the nucleotides G, A, T, C are labeled with different color labels. The DNA fragments of random length are size fractionated by polyacrylamide electrophoresis and the sequence is determined by the fluorescent label attached to each dideoxy nucleotide in an automated sequencing method. The manual method is a little more complex. An alternate method using chemicals to sequence DNA was developed by Maxim and Gilbert. Now, there are modern high throughput sequencing methods available and they are called as **Nextgen Sequencing**.

E. Polymerase chain reaction (PCR)

This method is used to amplify large amounts of DNA from small amounts of samples. This is used extensively in cloning new genes from small amounts of RNA or DNA and in forensics to identify a suspect by amplifying the DNA found in samples at the crime scene. This is an *in vitro* DNA synthesis reaction, in which two primers are used to synthesize DNA from a few copies of template using a thermostable DNA polymerase. This method includes a denaturation step, an annealing step and an extension step. The denaturation step, done at 90°C, separates the dsDNA template. The ssDNA anneals with the primer during the annealing step (55-70°C), and the annealed primer is extended by the DNA polymerase, incorporating dNTPs during the extension step. This whole process of denaturation, annealing and extension is repeated about 32 times, doubling the product each time, resulting in approximately up to 1 billion copies of the DNA fragment from each copy of the template.

11. Gene isolation, Characterization and Transfer

Gene isolation is done by construction of genomic DNA libraries or cDNA libraries. Genomic clones are DNA fragments containing the gene, including introns, exons, promoters and other noncoding regions. The cDNA includes only the coding region of a gene, because it is derived from a processed mRNA through reverse transcription.

A. Isolating genes and the study of genomics

Genes are isolated by first making a **genomic DNA or cDNA library** or from randomly amplified fragments through PCR. DNA library refers to a collection of several different DNA fragments constructed in a vector (plasmid or phage vectors) and maintained in a bacterial host. The whole library is screened using a radioactively labeled probe (a DNA fragment from a related gene or a synthetic DNA fragment based on protein sequences). The probe and the library DNA are denatured by alkali and renatured by neutralizing with an acid. During neutralization, specific clones which are highly complementary to the probe will anneal with the probe (called hybridization). These clones, present in individual bacterial colonies, are identified through the radioactivity of the probe and are isolated for further characterization. Once isolated, their DNA is isolated and sequenced.

In *genome projects*, the entire DNA sequence of the organism is completely sequenced. Prior to sequencing the entire genome, it has to be physically mapped using *genetic markers* that are associated with specific phenotypes and or sequences. Genomics refers to the analysis of the DNA and protein sequences. The analysis could be simply at the structural level (**structural genomics**) or at the functional level (**functional genomics**). Structural genomics includes computer analysis of DNA and protein sequences. The collection and analysis of biological sequence information is referred to as **bioinformatics**. Availability of extensive amounts of information and analysis of their structure and function will eventually lead to a detailed understanding of the role that genes play in shaping an organism or a species. With the advances in automated sequencing and analysis, this process will advance at a rapid rate in the coming decades.

B. Characterizing genes

Once genes are isolated, they need to be sequenced; the sequence is compared against known DNA and protein sequences in the DNA data banks. Then the genomic structure of the gene and its expression needs to be studied by Southern and Northern techniques.

1. Southern hybridization

This refers to hybridizing a labeled DNA probe to the target DNA sequences immobilized on a nylon membrane. The DNA bound to the membrane has been size fractionated on an agarose gel, denatured and then transferred to the membrane through either capillary action or electric transfer. Since this was discovered by E.M. Southern, it was named after him. The other methods were then named Northern (RNA-RNA hybridization) and Western (protein-antibody recognition) as variants of Southern.

Southern hybridization analysis is used to study the genome organization of a particular gene and determine the approximate number of copies of a specific gene. It is also used in RFLP analysis to find out if the restriction pattern of a particular gene differs between individuals. DNA-DNA hybridization techniques are commonly used in library screening and to find out if a particular gene is present in a genome or not.

2. Northern hybridization

This involves hybridizing a labeled DNA probe with size-fractionated RNA immobilized on a nylon membrane. This method is used to determine the RNA levels for a particular gene at different stages or in different tissues or organs of an organism.

3. Western hybridization

This involves protein-antibody interaction. A specific protein (antigen) is recognized first by a primary antibody which is then recognized by a secondary antibody conjugated to a fluorescent probe or an enzyme. The enzyme can convert a chromogenic substrate into a colored substance for the detection.

4. Microarray analysis

This helps in determining which genes are expressed among a group of several thousand genes that are placed on a small microscopic slide. The probe used to study the expression is fluorescent-labeled mRNA hybridized to fixed DNA samples on the slide.

C. Gene Transfer methods

Gene transfer from one organism to another is an important technique in the construction, maintenance, replication and expression of recombinant DNA in the transgenic organism. Such transformed organisms are commonly referred to as GMO—genetically modified organisms. To confirm the transformation, antibiotic marker genes are used to select for transformants that have become resistant to certain antibiotics that would normally kill untransformed cells. The following techniques summarize the different options available for transforming different types of organisms. The efficiency of transformation is measured by how many transformants are obtained per μg of DNA.

1. Bacterial transformation

Bacteria are transformed commonly by treating them with $CaCl_2$ or similar salts in solution and mixing them with recombinant DNA. A more efficient method is to electroporate the bacteria with DNA. Electroporation involves shooting a temporary short pulse of electricity through the bacteria, which then becomes permeable to foreign DNA. Alternatively, bacteria can be transfected using recombinant phages, which carry the desired DNA along with its essential DNA. This is used to construct DNA libraries.

2. Plant transformation

Plant transformation is done using cells that are embryonic or totipotent, which can be cultured under special conditions to regenerate completely new transformed plants. The most commonly used method of transformation of plants is by employing a bacterium called **Agrobacterium tumefaciens**, which can transfer a recombinant DNA plasmid into the plant cell and stably integrate it into its chromosome. This method works well for most dicots but monocots and some dicots are more difficult to transform. For such plants, an alternate method called **particle gun bombardment** is used. In this method gold particles coated with the recombinant DNA are physically shot into the cells using particle guns ("gene guns") specially designed for this purpose. Similar to bacterial transformants, the plant cells that are transformed are selected for using an antibiotic.

3. Animal transformatio

Isolated animal cells maintained in culture are transformed by salt-mediated transformation, transfection using phages, or electroporation. Sometimes microinjection is used to introduce DNA into large cells such as frog oocytes or other egg cells. Transformation of whole animals is done at the embryonic stage or at the egg or sperm level followed by fertilization, and then they are impregnated into a surrogate mother to regenerate a transformed animal.

III. Applications of Recombinant DNA Technology

A. Humans

This is a rapidly changing field with newer and newer applications being developed regularly and going through approval processes. Some applications include identification of genetic diseases by discovering the specific genes involved; diagnostics of diseases or infection such as HIV; development of recombinant vaccines by engineering various antigens in one plasmid to develop multiple vaccines; and gene therapy techniques to rectify genetic errors.

DNA detection techniques are extensively used in forensics and in paternity testing. Additionally, identification of new viruses such as the SARS (Severe Acute Respiratory Syndrome) virus is becoming routine. Other proteins that are important for human health such as insulin and growth hormones can be produced in bacteria. Recombinant DNA technology is also used in developing gene therapies. The human genome project is a major endeavor to sequence the entire genome to identify new genes for both general understanding and specific medical applications. As more and more applications become available to humans, several ethical issues need to be considered and will be discussed later.

B. Animals

Genetically engineering animals is not a major ethical issue and some applications of making novel proteins in animals have been developed by introducing genes at early embryonic stages. Some hormones are developed by recombinant DNA techniques to increase milk production (e.g.: bovine somatotropin; BST) or meat production. Vaccines are developed for animals to prevent some diseases that can be difficult to treat.

C. Plants

Plants are the first major organisms to see a vast application of recombinant DNA technology because of the ease of transformation and limited ethical issues involved, other than safety issues. Current applications include but are not limited to herbicide resistance, insect resistance, disease resistance and improved storage quality. Transgenic plants are being approved by the FDA (Food and Drug Administration) and are already showing up in the market place, e.g.: the Flavr-Savr tomato with long storage life, golden rice with high beta-carotene content, and insect- and herbicide-resistant crops.

IV. Safety and Bioethics

The major issues raised in recombinant DNA technology are related to the safety of both the scientists working in the laboratory and people consuming the product. Other issues include the ethical implications of both the development of such technology and its application on people.

A. Biological safety

The safety guidelines for recombinant DNA techniques were developed by the **NIH (National Institutes of Health)** and are periodically updated. It is important to follow the safety rules in a molecular biology laboratory to avoid contamination, infection, and mistakes, which have the potential to replicate quickly before they are even realized. Other potential dangers in a molecular biology laboratory include chemicals that can interfere with DNA and cause mutations and pathogenic viruses. One should be aware of the different chemicals, bacteria, viruses and other things used in a laboratory, and take adequate measures to protect laboratory workers from potential health hazards.

The safety of the public, who are exposed to such recombinant products, is the responsibility of the the **FDA (Food and Drug Administration)**, which studies each product rigorously for potential safety issues for the consumer. Industries also play a role in recommending certain procedures to be followed before approval. Some products or procedures involving the release of recombinant organisms into the environment are tested by the **EPA (Environmental Protections Agency)**. The genetically modified crops are regulated by **USDA (United States Department of Agriculture)**. These new genetically modified crops and animals have been found safe by the FDA and USDA. However, some side effects may not be known until the product is available to the masses.

B. Ethical issues

Consideration of ethical issues is critical in both the development of and the implications of recombinant DNA technology as we saw before. It is important to consider before starting a project whether it is ethical to do such research. Examples include the use of fetal tissues for biological research and cloning humans by artificially replicating zygotes before implantation into surrogate mothers. Even though the techniques are available to do such research, especially the latter, the research has been stopped because of ethical concerns. The second issue is regarding the implications. For example, the availability of a vast amount of DNA sequence information on genetic diseases may prompt insurance agencies and employers to screen out people with potential genetic disorders. This is called *genetic discrimination*. How would we control the use and misuse of such information?

The examples of "Dolly" the sheep and "Gene" the cow that were cloned from a single cell have raised serious concerns that it might lead to human cloning one day. Technologies are being developed to manufacture human body parts in laboratories to be used for transplantation. Is it ethical to use adult stem cells for research but not embryonic stem cells? Time will tell which ethical and safety concerns will remain or change with the times.

CELL AND MOLECULAR BIOLOGY
COURSE GUIDE

Worksheets

WORKSHEET NUMBER	CHAPTERS COVERED
1	Introduction and Chemistry for Biology
2	Biological Molecules
3	Cell Structure and Function, Biological Membranes and Origin of Life
4	Introduction to Metabolism
5	Respiration
6	Photosynthesis
7	Cell Division – Mitosis and Meiosis
8	Mendelian Genetics
9	DNA Structure and Replication
10	Transcription and Translation
11	Regulation of Gene Expression
12	Recombinant DNA Technology

WORSHEET 1
Introduction, Atoms and Molecules, Water, and Organic Compounds

Name Reese Brinkley

A. Multiple Choice questions

1. All living things have the following properties EXCEPT
   a. they are made of cells.
   b. they respond to environmental stimuli.
   c. they are composed of carbon, hydrogen, oxygen, and nitrogen.
   d. they have active metabolisms.
   e. they have a nucleus containing chromosomes.

2. The unicellular eukaryotic cells belong to which kingdom?
   a. Monera   b. Protista   c. Plantae
   d. Fungi   e. Animalian

3. The study of cellular and molecular biology is important because
   a. everyone in natural sciences must take this course.
   b. most graduate students study genes and development.
   c. DNA was discovered recently, so we all should learn more about this subject.
   d. many biological phenomena are better understood at the cellular and molecular levels.
   e. more than half a million papers are published in biology per year.

4. Two families belonging to the same mammalian class must also belong to same
   a. family   b. genus   c. order   d. species   e. phylum

5. A chlorine atom has the following number of valence electrons.
   a. 7   b.5   c.3   d.4   e.2

6. According to the octet rule, atoms with eight electrons in their valence shell tend to
   a. form ionic bonds with other atoms.
   b. be very reactive with other atoms.
   c. be biologically very important.
   d. be particularly stable and inert.
   e. form covalent bonds in aqueous solutions.

7. When the pH of Trizma base is adjusted from 10 to 8, the H^+ ion concentration changes
   a. 2 fold.   b. 10 fold.   c. 100 fold.   d. 1000 fold.   e. 3 fold.

8. The electronegativity of oxygen is 3.5 compared to 2.1 of hydrogen (H). Which of the following statements is correct about water (H_2O)?
   a. Each hydrogen atom has a partial positive charge.
   b. The oxygen atom has a strong positive charge.
   c. Each hydrogen atom has a slight negative charge.
   d. The oxygen atom has a partial positive charge.
   e. There are covalent bonds between the hydrogen atoms.

9. Atoms with one electron in their first shell (such as Na) and another atom (such as Cl) with seven electrons in their valence shell will form
   a. H-bond
   b. ionic bonds
   c. polar covalent bond
   d. non-polar covalent bond
   e. hydrophobic interaction

10.   The base pairing of G-C and A-T in a double helix of DNA are due to _____
       a. covalent bonds.
       b. ionic bonds.
       c. H-bonds.
       d. Van der Waals forces.
       e. hydrophobic interactions.

11.   Assume that acid rain has lowered the pH of a particular lake to pH 5.0. What is the hydroxide ion concentration of this lake?
                     1. 1×10^{-5} moles of hydroxide ion per liter of lake water
                     2. 1×10^{-9} moles of hydroxide ion per liter of lake water
                     3. 5.0 molar with regard to hydroxide ion concentration
                     4. 9.0 molar with regard to hydroxide ion concentration
       a. 1
       b. 2
       c. 3
       d. 4
       e. Both 2 and 4 are correct.

B. SHORT ANSWER QUESTIONS

1.   List all the chemical bonds and interactions. Give at least one example for each. Make sure to include a biological molecule in the examples. Draw four molecules which shows polar and non-polar covalent bond, H-bond and ionic bond.

2. Draw the functional groups and list examples of molecules with such functional group. Group them in terms of polar or nonpolar and acidic or basic.

WORKSHEET 2
Biological Molecules

Name _____

A. Multiple-choice questions

. The functional group shown below is found in which of the following macromolecules?

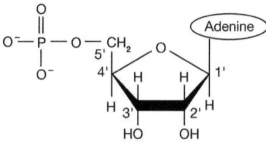

a. DNA   b. cellulose   c. starch
d. RNA   e. fatty acid

. The macromolecule consisting of the monomer shown in the figure below is
a. starch   b. carotenoid   c. chitinase
d. DNA   e. RNA

. The tertiary structure of a protein is the
a. folding of proteins into an alpha helix and beta sheets.
b. regular, repeated bonding between the -C=O group and the -NH group.
c. irregular bonding between the side chains of amino acids.
d. folding of several subunits of a complex protein.
e amino acid sequence of a polypeptide.

. The following polysaccharide has beta 1,4 linkage and is hard for humans to digest.
a. glycogen
b. fructose
c. starch
d. cellulose
e. collagen

. Condensation synthesis is involved in which of the following?
a.   Break down of starch for energy
b.   Hydrogen bond formation between nucleic acids
c.   Glycosidic bond formation of carbohydrates
d.   The hydrophilic interactions of lipids
e.   The digestion of maltose to glucose

. A 14 Carbon-long hydrocarbon chain with a C=C double bond between the third and fourth carbon and carboxyl
group at one end is a
a. saturated fatty acid.   b. polyunsaturated fatty acid.
c. steroid.   d. monounsaturated fatty acid.
e. triglyceride.

7. The chemical structure shown below is a major component of
   a. cell walls.   b. plasma membranes.
   c. chromosomes.   d. ribosomes.
   e. DNA.

$$\begin{array}{c} H \\ | \\ H-C-O-C- \text{ Fatty acid 1} \\ | \quad\quad O \\ | \quad\quad || \\ H-C-O-C- \text{ Fatty acid 2} \\ | \quad\quad O \\ | \quad\quad || \\ H-C-O-P-O-R \\ | \quad\quad | \\ H \quad\quad O^- \end{array}$$

8. Some proteases contain amino acids containing -OH groups in their active sites. Whihc of the following amino acids contain -OH groups in their side chains?
   a. Valine, leucine, isoleucine
   b. Serine, threonine, tyrosine
   c. Glycine, alanine, methionine
   d. Aspartic acid, glutamic acid
   e. Lysine, arginine, histidine

9. What is the major purpose of RNA?
   a. transmit genetic information to offspring.
   b. function in the synthesis of proteins.
   c. make a copy of itself, thus insuring genetic continuity.
   d. act as a pattern to form DNA.
   e. form the genes of an organism.

10. What is a triacylglycerol?
   a. A protein with tertiary structure
   b. A lipid made of three fatty acids and glycerol
   c. A kind of lipid that makes up much of the plasma membrane
   d. A molecule formed from three alcohols
   e. A carbohydrate with three sugars

11. All of the following nitrogenous bases are found in DNA EXCEPT
   a. thymine.   b. adenine.   c. uracil.
   d. guanine.   e. cytosine.

12. All of the following items are found in the bases of RNA EXCEPT
   a. sulfur.   b. adenine.   c. uracil.
   d. phosphate.   e. cytosine.

B. Short Answer Questions

1. Make a concept map of biological molecules. Start with Carbohydrates, Lipids, Proteins, and Nucleic acids on the top and the specific examples at the bottom. There will be three or four levels of this concept map. Include the monomers in each group and the types of bonds in each macromolecule (underline or highlight the macromolecules only).

Biological Molecules

	Carbohydrates	Lipids	Proteins	Nucleic Acids
Monomers	Monosaccharides	Glycerol, Fatty Acids, Isoprene units	Amino Acid	nucleotides
Bond-connecting Monomers	Glycogen	ester	Peptide	Phosphodiester
Subgroups	Mon-di-poly soccurides	Fats, phospholipids, Steriods, caretenoids	Soluble, Membrane	DNA, RNA
Examples				

Draw one monomer for each group.

2. List all the key terms (bold faced) from this biological molecules chapter and their meanings. Use more sheets if needed.

Key Term	Meaning
Carbohydrates	
Lipids	
Proteins	
Nucleic Acids	

WORKSHEET 3
Cell Structure and Function, Biological Membranes, and Origin of Life

Name _____

A. Multiple Choice Questions.

1.   Proteins are sometimes modified by glycosylation (adding oligosaccharides) and sorted out in
    a. chloroplasts.   b. mitochondria.   c. amyloplasts.
    d. peroxisomes.   e. the Golgi apparatus.

2.   Ribosomes are assembled in the
    a. nucleolus.   b. glyoxysomes.   c. smooth ER.
    d. rough ER.   e. mitochondria.

3.   Which of the following microscopes is the best to study the shape and color of small algal cells?
    a. bright field light microscope   b. transmission electron microscope
    c. scanning electron microscope   d. magnifying glass
    e. dissection microscope

4.   Steroid hormones are made in
    a. ribosomes.   b. the rough ER.   c. the smooth ER.
    d. vacuoles.   e. peroxisomes.

5.   Which structure in peanut seeds converts storage lipids into carbohydrates in growing seedlings?
    a. Chromosomes   b. Desmosomes   c. Plasmodesmata
    d. Vacuoles   e. Glyoxysomes

6.   Which of the following would be found in a bacterial cell wall that can be degraded by lysozyme?
    a. NAM-NAG   b. NAG alone   c. Cellulose
    d. Starch   e. Lignin

7.   Which structure in plant cells facilitates intercellular transport?
    a. Peroxisomes   b. Desmosomes   c. Plasmodesmata
    d. Glyoxysomes   e. Tight junctions

8.   Which of the following is capable of using stored carbohydrates to make ATP?
    a. Chloroplasts   b. Mitochondria   c. Leucoplasts
    d. Peroxisomes   e. Golgi apparatus

9.   Which of the following is the correct sequence of plant cell wall layers, beginning with the outside and progressing inward to the plasma membrane?
    a. Middle lamella, secondary wall, primary wall
    b. Middle lamella, primary wall, secondary wall
    c. Secondary wall, primary wall, middle lamella
    d. Primary wall, middle lamella, secondary wall
    e. Secondary wall, middle lamella, primary wall

10.   Cells can be described as having a "cytoskeleton" of internal structures that contribute to the shape, organization, and movement of the cell. All of the following are part of the "cytoskeleton" EXCEPT
    a. the cell wall.
    b. microtubules.
    c. microfilaments.
    d. intermediate filaments.
    e. actin.

11. Whihc of the following can rapidly go through a lipid part of the bilayer?
    a. Glucose   b. Ca^{++} c. Na^+ d. water   e. steroid hormone

12. The transport of molecules against the concentration gradient using energy is called
    a. passive transport.　　　b. lateral transport.　　　c. active transport.
    d. symport.　　　　　　　e. uniport.

13. A person visiting an emergency room is given distilled water instead of saline solution intravenously. What will happen to his red blood cells? They will _____
    a. be stable.　　　　　　b. shrivel.　　　　　　　c. swell and burst.
    d. be flaccid.　　　　　　e. be turgid.

14. A plant growing in colder climate will have more unsaturated lipids than a plant in tropical climate because the
    a. greater the unsaturation, the lower the fluidity.
    b. greater the unsaturation, the higher the melting temperature.
    c. lower the unsaturation, the greater the fluidity.
    d. greater the unsaturation, the greater the fluidity.
    e. cold weather people like plants with high amounts of unsaturated fatty acids.

15. An example of a protein that is a cotransport, a symport, and a secondary active transport is
    a. H^+ pump.
    b. Na^+-K^+ pump.
    c. H^+- sucrose pump.
    d. glucose transporter.
    e. cystine transporter.

16. Uptake of LDL-cholesterol from the blood stream is an example of
    a. parasitosis.　　　　　　　b. phagocytocis.
    c. exocytosis.　　　　　　　d. pinocytosis.
    e. receptor mediated endocytosis.

17. Some stomach cells transport chloride ions inside and transport bicarbonate ions outside the cell, which is done by same transport protein. Such a transport mechanism is called a
    a. antiport.　　　　　　　b. symport.　　　　　　c. uniport.
    d. cotransport.　　　　　　e. biport.

18. The function of cholesterol molecules in a lipid bilayer is to
    a. bind the membrane together.　　　　　b. disrupt transport of ions.
    c. attach to carbohydrates.　　　　　　d. attach to glycoproteins.
    e. maintain the membrane fluidity.

19. Which of the following is the correct sequence of events in the origin of life?
    I.　Synthesis of organic monomers
    II.　Formation of prebiotic structures
    III.　Synthesis of organic polymers
    IV. Formation of reproducible cells

    a. III, II, I, IV　b. I, II, IV, III　　c. IV, III, I, II　　d. I, III, II, IV　　e. II, III, I , IV

20. The genetic material that was considered to have formed first because of the evidence that
    a.　It was widely found on primitive earth
    b.　it can serve as monomers for protein synthesis
    c.　it can store information and act as a enzyme to catalyze reactions.
    d.　it was stable and double stranded to avoid degradation.
    e.　it was made of deoxyribonucleotides.

B. Short Answer Questions

1. Draw the structure of a bacterial cell, plant cell and animal cell and label the contents.

2. Write the presence and function of the following cell components.

CELL COMPONENT	PRESENT IN			MAJOR FUNCTION(S)
	Bacteria	Plants	Animals	
1. Cell wall				
2. Plasma membrane				
3. Nucleus				
4. Ribosomes				
5. Smooth ER				
6. Rough ER				
7. Chloroplast				
8. Mitochondria				
9. Lysosomes				
10. Peroxisomes				
11. Glyoxysomes				
12. Central vacuole				
13. Cytoskeleton elements				
14. Plasmodesmata				
15. Desmosomes				
16. Tight junctions				

3. Make a <u>concept map of</u> Cellular Transport Mechanisms for small and large molecules. Include the terms, active transport, passive transport, facilitated transport, simple diffusion, osmosis, exocytosis, endocytosis.

4. Draw the time line of major events in the origin and evolution of life on earth.

5. Write the fact that is most convincing to you about the chemical origin of life and how you can substantiate that with experiments or additional evidence.

WORKSHEET 4
Introduction to Metabolism

Name _____

A. Multiple-Choice Questions

1. Burning of methane gas (CH_4 + 2 O_2 --> CO_2 + 2 H_2O + 160 kCal/mol energy) is an example of a/an
   a. exothermic reaction.
   b. endothermic reaction.
   c. endergonic reaction.
   d. cooling reaction.
   e. anabolic reaction.

2. Roundup herbicide is a competitive inhibitor of the enzyme EPSP-synthase in an amino acid biosynthesis pathway. Roundup can alter the
   a. *Vmax* of this enzyme.
   b. *Km* for its substrate(s).
   c. both a and b.
   d. regulatory site in enzyme.
   e. none of the above.

3. The change in free energy (ΔG) is best explained by the following equation.
   a. $\Delta G = \Delta H + T\Delta S$
   b. $\Delta G = \Delta H - T\Delta S$
   c. $\Delta G = \Delta H + T - \Delta S$
   d. $\Delta G = T\Delta S - \Delta H$
   e. $\Delta G = \Delta H - T + \Delta S$

4. ATP is utilized in driving much cellular work because it
   a. uses lots of bond energy for hydrolysis.
   b. absorbs heat and make the body cool.
   c. releases free energy during hydrolysis.
   d. it helps in releasing O_2 from photosynthesis.
   e. is an anabolic process important for survival.

5. Enzymes are biological catalysts that can increase the rate of a biochemical reaction by
   a. increasing entropy and enthalpy.
   b. denaturing the reactants.
   c. decreasing the concentration of reactants.
   d. lowering the energy of activation.
   e. increasing the free energy of activation.

6. Acetoacetate synthase is a key regulatory enzyme in the beginning of the valine biosynthetic pathway. When valine accumulates above a specific concentration, it inhibits the activity of acetoacetate synthase. The mechanism of action of valine is
   a. competitive inhibition.
   b. noncompetitive inhibition.
   c. feedback regulation.
   d. chemical modification.
   e. irreversible inhibition.

Use the graph below to answer questions 7 and 8.

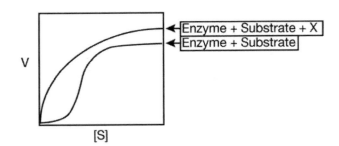

7.   Which of the following statements is true about the enzyme used in the above study?
     a. It shows cooperativity.
     b. It is a complex enzyme.
     c. It shows a sigmoidal response.
     d. It is an allosteric enzyme.
     e. All of the above

8.   Based on the above graph, we can tell that compound-X is a/an
     a. competitive inhibitor.
     b. non-competitive inhibitor.
     c. activator.
     d. irreversible inhibitor.
     e. feedback inhibitor.

9.   Phosphoglucomutase catalyzes the isomerization reaction of converting glucose 6-phosphate (G6P) to fructose 6-phosphate (F6P). You are starting the reaction in a test tube with the 0.8 mM substrate (G6P), and you let the reaction reach equilibrium. The product (F6P) concentration at equilibrium is 0.6 mM. There are no intermediates in this reaction and no products at the beginning. The Keq for this reaction is
     a. 1.5   b. 0.75   c. 2.0   d. 3.0   e. 4.0

10. Both NAD^+ and FAD are
     a. enzymes.   b. organic cofactors.
     c. inorganic cofactors.   d. reducing agents.
     e. amino acids.

11. The first law of thermodynamics states that the energy
     a. can neither be created nor destroyed.
     b. the total energy of the universe is constant.
     c. the energy can be transferred or transformed.
     d. a, b, and c are correct.
     e. The energy transfer results in increased entropy.

12. Enzyme activity can be regulated by all the following EXCEPT
     a. activators.
     b. competitive inhibitors.
     c. noncompetitive inhibitors.
     d. phosphorylation.
     e. degradation.

B. Short Answer Questions.

1. Give an example of exergonic reaction and an example of endergonic reaction happening inside your cells.

2. Give an example of a spontaneous reaction that results in a decrease in entropy.

3. Give an example of a spontaneous (exergonic) reaction that is endothermic.

C. Define the following terms

1. Free Energy

2. Entropy

3. Enthalpy

4. Exergonic reaction

5. Endothermic reaction

6. ATP

7. Energy coupling

8. Vmax

9. Km

10. Competitive inhibition

11. Non-competitive inhibition

12. Active site

13. Allosteric enzyme

14. Feedback Inhibition

15. Phosphorylation

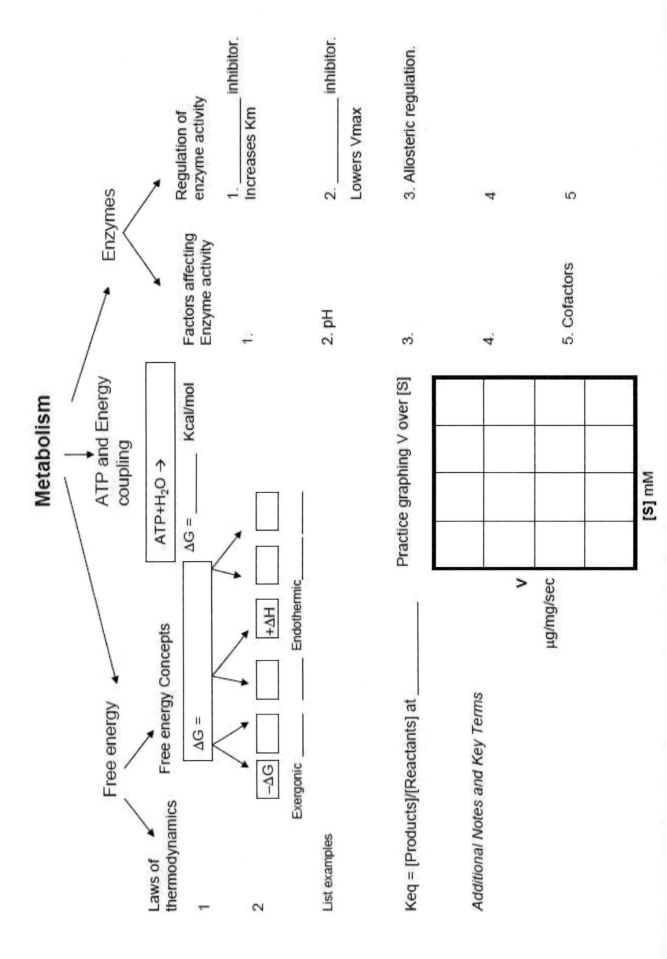

Metabolism

Enzymes

ATP and Energy coupling

Free energy

Free energy Concepts

Laws of thermodynamics

1

2

Regulation of enzyme activity

1. _____ inhibitor.
   Increases Km

2. _____ inhibitor.
   Lowers Vmax

3. Allosteric regulation.

4

5

Factors affecting Enzyme activity

1.

2. pH

3.

4.

5. Cofactors

ATP+H_2O →

ΔG = _____ Kcal/mol

ΔG =

$-\Delta G$ $+\Delta H$

Exergonic _____ Endothermic _____

List examples

Practice graphing V over [S] _____

[S] mM

V
μg/mg/sec

Keq = [Products]/[Reactants] at _____

Additional Notes and Key Terms

Name _____

A. Multiple-Choice Questions

1. The following reaction results in

$$\begin{array}{c} OH \\ | \\ C=O \\ | \\ C-O{\sim}P \\ \| \\ CH_2 \end{array} + ADP \longrightarrow \begin{array}{c} OH \\ | \\ C=O \\ | \\ C=O \\ | \\ CH_3 \end{array} + ATP$$

PEP   Pyruvate

  a. oxidative phosphorylation.   b. substrate-level phosphorylation.
  c. chemosmosis.   d. reduction.
  e. oxidation.

Use the following choices for questions 2 through 5. The choices may appear once, more than once or not at all.
  a. glycolysis
  b. Krebs cycle
  c. oxidative phosphorylation
  d. lactic acid fermentation
  e. alcohol fermentation

2. The metabolic process most closely associated with intracellular membranes is _____.

3. The metabolic pathway that makes $FADH_2$ and occurs in mitochondria is _____.

4. The frothing of beer is due to the CO_2 released during _____.

5. Fast-twitch muscle fibers under stress generate a quick burst of energy and regenerate NAD^+ mostly through

   _____.

6. The key regulatory enzyme in glycolysis is
  a. phosphofructokinase.
  b. pyruvate dehydrogenase.
  c. citrate synthase.
  d. isocitrate dehydrogenase.
  e. PEP carboxylase.

7. The end-products of glycolysis under aerobic conditions are
  a. ATP, CO_2, and water.   b. NADH, ATP, and pyruvate.
  c. pyruvate, ADP, and NAD^+.   d. $FADH_2$, NAD^+, and ATP.
  e. pyruvate, NADH, and $FADH_2$.

8. While brewing beer, 2,000 moles of glucose was used. How many moles of ATP will be made (at least) in this process?
  a. 4,000   b. 8,000   c. 20,000
  d. 60,000   e. 64,000

9. The outputs of the Krebs cycle that transfer energy to the electron transport system are
  a. ATP and GTP.
  b. CO_2 and GTP.
  c. $FADH_2$ and NADH.
  d. NADH and ATP.
  e. $FADH_2$ and ATP.

10. Which of the following statements is <u>true</u> of alcohol fermentation?
    a. It regenerates NAD^+ with a net gain of 2 ATP per glucose.
    b. It produces a net gain of NADH only.
    c. It consumes O_2 and releases CO_2.
    d. It can be performed only by bacteria.
    e. It produces more than 30 to 32 ATP per glucose

11. The first committed product of the Krebs cycle is
    a. acetyl CoA.   b. oxaloacetate.   c. citrate.
    d. isocitrate.   e. pyruvate.

12. The first committed step in Glycolysis is catalyzed by which of the following enzyme?
    a. Phosphofructokinase
    b. Pyruvate decarboxylase
    c. Triose phosphate isomerase
    d. Isocitrate dehydrogenase
    e. Hexokinase

13. Catabolism of lipids and carbohydrates can result in the formation of _____, which enters the Krebs cycle.
    What is this product?
    a. glucose   b. acetyl CoA   c. fatty acids
    d. amino acids   e. isocitrate

14. The rate limiting enzyme in Krebs cycle is
    a. phosphofructokinase
    b. pyruvate dehydrogenase
    c. triose phosphate isomerase
    d. isocitrate dehydrogenase
    e. hexokinase

B. Short Answer Questions
1. Identify <u>all</u> the inputs and outputs of the glycolysis, acetyl CoA formation, Krebs cycle, and oxidative phosphorylation. What are the regulatory steps of these pathways and what do the key regulatory enzymes control? What compounds inhibit/activate these enzymes?

	Glycolysis	Acetyl CoA Formation	Krebs Cycle	Oxidative Phosphorylation
Location inside an eukaryotic cell				
Net Inputs				
Net Outputs				<u>Respiratory poisons.</u>
Key Regulatory Steps and Enzymes				

3. Given that 5 moles of glucose are completely metabolized under aerobic conditions, calculate how many moles of ATP will be made by substrate-level and oxidative phosphorylation in each stage of respiration (glycolysis, Kreb's cycle, and oxidative phosphorylation.).

4. If a fatty acid is broken down to 2 moles of acetyl CoAs through beta -oxidation and they enter Krebs cycle, how many moles of ATPs will be made by substrate-level and oxidative phosphorylation in each stage of respiration? (Remember acetyl CoA enters at Krebs Cycle)

5. List the inputs and outputs of alcohol fermentation and lactate fermentation.

C. Complete this concept map of the aerobic respiration chapter and include all relevant details

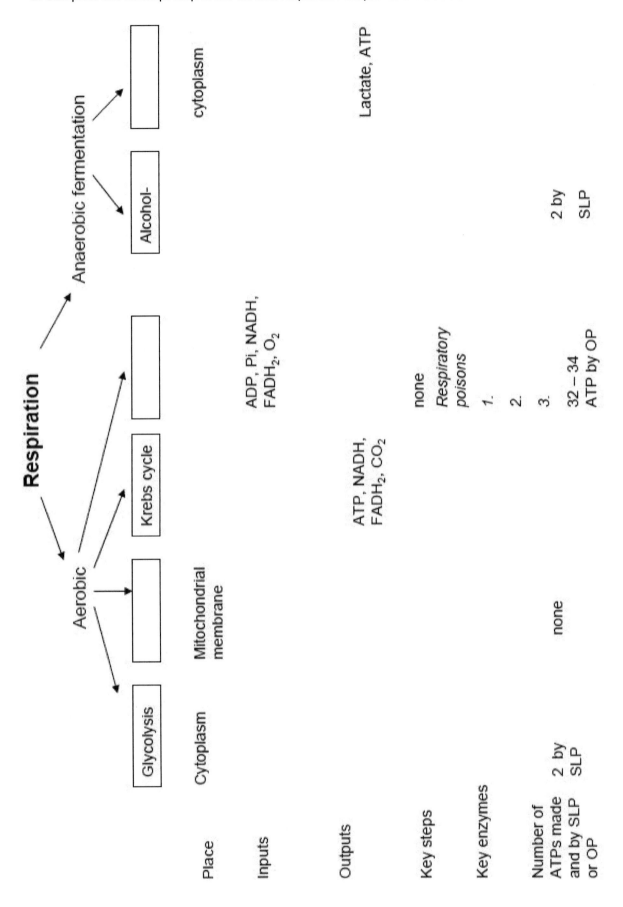

Respiration

Anaerobic fermentation

[ ]   cytoplasm

Alcohol-

Lactate, ATP

Aerobic

Glycolysis   Krebs cycle   [ ]   [ ]

Place   Cytoplasm   Mitochondrial
                                 membrane

Inputs   ADP, Pi, NADH,
                                                FADH₂, O₂

Outputs   ATP, NADH,
                 FADH₂, CO₂

Key steps   none
                                                Respiratory
                                                poisons
                                                1.
                                                2.
                                                3.

Key enzymes

Number of   2 by   none   32 – 34   2 by
ATPs made   SLP   ATP by OP   SLP
and by SLP
or OP

WORKSHEET 6
Photosynthesis

Name _____

A. Multiple-Choice Questions

1. The rice plants grown in Texas and Louisiana are examples of
   a. C_3 plants.
   b. C_4 plants.
   c. CAM plants.
   d. exotic plants.
   e. dicot plants

2. Why are C_4 and CAM plants able to photosynthesize with no apparent photorespiration?
   a. They do not carry out the Calvin cycle.
   b. They use a more efficient enzyme initially to fix CO_2.
   c. They are adapted to cold, wet climates.
   d. They conserve water more efficiently.
   e. They exclude oxygen from their tissues.

3. Which of the following are products of the Calvin cycle and are utilized in the light reactions of photosynthesis?
   a. CO_2 and glucose
   b. H_2O and O_2
   c. ADP, Pi, and $NADP^+$
   d. Electrons and H^+
   e. Both c and d are correct.

4. The reactions of the Calvin cycle require all of the following molecules EXCEPT
   a. CO_2.
   b. ATP.
   c. RuBP.
   d. ADP and Pi
   e. NADPH.

5. You have just discovered a new flower species that has a unique photosynthetic pigment. The leaves of this plant appear to be reddish yellow. What wave lengths of visible light are not being absorbed by this pigment?
   a. Red and yellow
   b. Blue and violet
   c. Green and yellow
   d. Blue, green, and red
   e. Green, blue, and violet

6. The reactions of the Calvin cycle stops when you move the plants from light to dark condition because this process needs
   a. ATP.
   b. NADPH
   c. glucose.
   d. ATP and NADPH.
   e. ATP and glucose

7. In C_4 plants, carbon fixation takes place in the _____ cells, and then the CO_2 is transferred as malic or aspartic acid to _____ cells where carbon dioxide is released for entry into the Calvin cycle.
   a. mesophyll; bundle sheath
   b. stomatal; mesophyll
   c. bundle sheath; epidermal
   d. epidermal; mesophyll
   e. stomatal; epidermal

8. When a chlorophyll molecule in photosystem I traps light, it loses a pair of electrons to ultimately reduce NADP to NADPH. In non-cyclic electron flow, these electrons are replaced by
    a. by electrons from one of the antenna pigments.
    b. by electrons from the other end of photosystem I.
    c. by a transfer from photosystem II.
    d. by a transfer from an unexcited chlorophyll molecule.
    e. by electrons from one of the hydrogen atoms in NADPH.

9. Which of the following does not regulate of ribulose bisphosphate carboxylase (RuBisCO)?
    a. pH
    b. temperature
    c. concentration of RuBP
    d. concentration of ATP
    e. concentration of both O_2 and CO_2

10. Where does the Calvin cycle of photosynthesis take place?
    a. Stroma of the chloroplast
    b. Thylakoid membrane
    c. Cytoplasm surrounding the chloroplast
    d. Chlorophyll molecule
    e. Outer membrane of the chloroplast

B. Short Answer Questions

1. What are the inputs and outputs of cyclic and non-cyclic electron transfer in light reactions? Where do the inputs come from and outputs go to? Complete a similar table for the Calvin cycle.

	Cyclic Electron Transfer	Non-cyclic Electron Transfer
Net Inputs		
Source of input		
Net Outputs		
Outputs go to		

	Calvin Cycle
Net Inputs	
Source of input	
Net Outputs	
Outputs go to	

2. Draw the noncyclic electron transfer (Z-diagram) and mark the inputs and outputs in different colors.

3. What is the key regulatory enzyme in Calvin cycle and how is it regulated?

4. List the three variations of carbon-fixation reactions (C3, C4, and CAM) and write their basic characteristics (locations or times of C4 and C3 pathway in each) with one or two examples for each.

5. Complete the following concept map on photosynthesis.

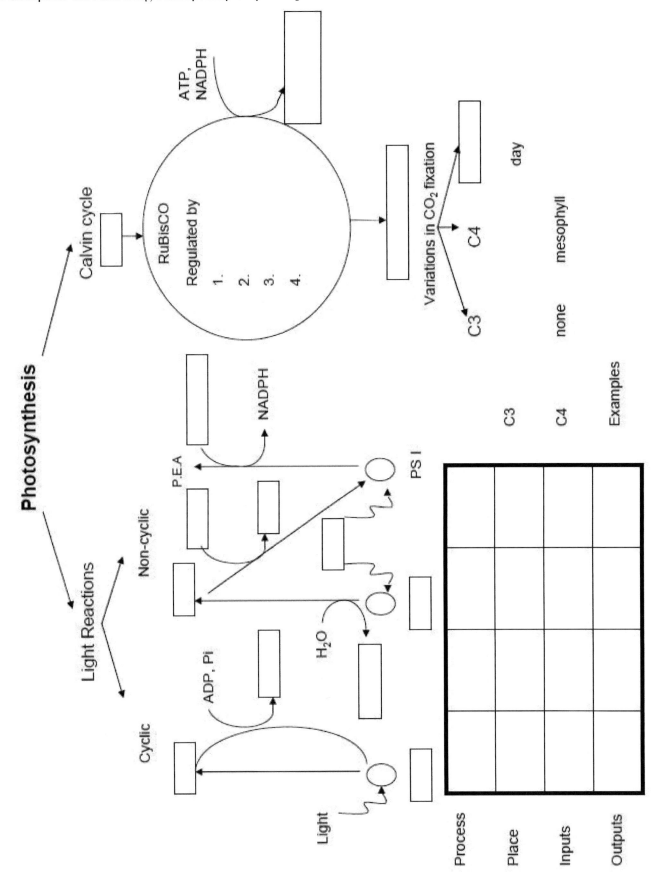

Worksheet 7
Mitosis & Meiosis

Name _____

A.   Multiple choice questions

1.   The two strands of a replicated chromosome during prometaphase is called
     a. sister chromatids
     b. centrosome
     c. homologs
     d. chromatin
     e. chromosomes

2.   Compared to the parent cell, each daughter cell derived from <u>mitosis</u> will
     a. contain half the number of chromosomes and half the amount of DNA
     b. contain half the chromosome number and identical DNA sequence.
     c. contain twice the chromosome number and identical DNA sequence.
     d. be identical in chromosome number but differ in DNA sequence.
     e. be identical in chromosome number and DNA sequence.

3.   The chromosomes appear and nuclear envelope disappears during
     a. metaphase
     b. prophase
     c. S-phase
     d. telophase
     e. anaphase

4.   A cell dividing with cleavage furrow, nucleus and other cytoplasmic contents including mitochondria and ribosomes
     is likely to be
     a.   bacterial cell
     b.   tree cell
     c.   plant cell
     d.   animal cell
     e.   none of these

5.   During meiosis the **homologs** separate from each other during
     a.   metaphaseI
     b.   prophaseI
     c.   prophase II
     a.   anaphase II
     e.   anaphaseI

6.   When does a synapsis and crossing over happen?
     a. during prophase I of meiosis
     b. during fertilization or fusion of gametes
     c. during metaphase II of meiosis
     d. during prophase of mitosis
     e. during metaphase of mitosis

7.   You are genetically unique. This is a result of
     a.   random fertilization
     b.   genetic recombination.
     c.   mutation.
     d.   random assortment of parental chromosomes
     e.   all the above

8. During meiosis the **sister chromatids** separate from each other during
    a. metaphase I
    b. prophase I
    c. prophase II
    d. anaphase II
    e. anaphase I

9. When does DNA synthesis occur in gametogenesis (generation of gametes)?
    a. Before prophase I
    b. During fertilization of gametes
    c. During Gap 2
    d. Before prophase II
    e. Both A and D are correct

10. The phases of meiosis that cause the most variation in the four daughter cells are
    a. prophase I and telophase II.
    b. prophase II and anaphase II.
    c. metaphase I and telophase II.
    d. anaphase I and prophase II.
    e. prophase I and metaphase I.

11. The diploid stage of an adult animal is maintained as a result of _____
    a. random fertilization
    b. genetic recombination.
    c. mutation.
    d. random assortment
    e. gamete formation

12. The number of sets of chromosomes in a diploid animal liver cell will be _____ that of gametes
    a. same as
    b. twice
    c. one half
    d. four times
    e. one tenth

B. Short Answer Questions

1. Write the specific events that happen during the different stages (G1, S, G2 and M phases) of cell cycle.

2. In the given Table, draw the different stages of <u>mitosis</u> and write key events that will happen in each of them.

Drawings of each stage	Description of major events

3. List the major events that happen in each of the following stages in <u>Meiosis I and II.</u>

Interphase I	
Prophase I	
MetaphaseI	
Anaphase I	
Telophase and cytokinesis I	
Interphase II	
Prophase II	
Metaphase II	
Anaphase II	
Telophase and cytokinesis II	

4. Write the meaning of the following key terms listed in column A.
   Add more key terms in on additional pages, if necessary.

Key Terms	Related Information
Binary fission	
Chromatids	
Chromatin	
Chromosome	
Meiosis	
G1-phase	
S -phase	
G2- phase	
MTOC	
Metaphase plate	
Kinetochore	
Spindle fibers	
Cleavage furrow	
Cell Plate	
Cyclin	
Cdk or Cdc2	
Proto-oncogene	
Oncogene	
Metastasis	
Telomerase	

Worksheet 8
Mendelian Genetics

Name _____

A. Multiple Choice Questions

1. A cross between homozygous purple-flowered and homozygous white-flowered pea plants results in all offspring with purple flowers. This demonstrates
   a. true-breeding.
   b. the blending model of genetics.
   c. dominance.
   d. a dihybrid cross.
   e. the mistakes made by Mendel.

2. A couple who are both carriers of the gene for cystic fibrosis have their first child who have cystic fibrosis. What is the probability that their next child will be a carrier for cystic fibrosis but not have the disease?
   a. 0%   b. 50%   c. 25%   d. 100%   e. 75%

3. In crossing a homozygous recessive with a heterozygote, what is the chance of getting an offspring with the homozygous dominant phenotype?
   a. 0%   b. 75%   c. 25%   d. 100%   e. 50%

4. Albinism (lack of skin pigmentation) is caused by a recessive autosomal allele. A normal man and an albino woman, have a normal child together. What is the chance of their next child born an albino?
   a. 0%
   b. 25%
   c. 50%
   d. 75%
   e. 100%

5. A 3:1 phenotypic ratio is characteristic of
   a. linked genes.
   b. a dihybrid cross.
   c. a monohybrid cross.
   d. a trihybrid cross.
   e. Recessive nature.

6. A man who carries an X-linked disorder will pass it on to
   a. all of his children.
   b. all of his daughters.
   c. all of his sons.
   d. half of his daughters.
   e. half of his sons.

7. Which of the following summarizes the relationship between events in meiosis and the "law of independent segregation" for alleles?
   a. Independent chromosomal assortment, results in independent allele segregation if the genes are on different chromosomes
   b. Genes on the same chromosome assort independently if they are physically located far away from each other and have gone through recombination
   c. Alleles do not get exchanged during chromosomal assortment
   d. There is no relation between the two
   e. Both a & b above

B. Short Answer Questions

1.   Draw Punnet Squares for a monohybrid cross. Label the genotypes and phenotypes.

2.   List the types of non-mendelian inheritance patterns and examples for each of them.

3.   List six human diseases that are either dominantly or recessively inherited.

Worksheet 9
DNA Structure and Replication

Name _____

A. Multiple-Choice Questions

1. Chargaff's rules were confirmed after Watson and Crick elucidated the double helical structure of DNA by the fact that
   a. the strands of DNA are antiparallel.
   b. ribose-phosphate forms the backbone of DNA.
   c. the double helix is right-handed.
   d. the nitrogenous bases are in the middle.
   e. A base-pairs with T and G base-pairs with C.

2. Hershey and Chase grew some T$_2$ phages in ^{32}P-containing medium and then used that phage to infect a bacterial culture. After the infection they detached the phage heads from the bacteria by using a blender. Then they centrifuged the culture to separate the bacterial pellet and the supernatant. Which of the following fraction will be the most radioactive?
   a. Supernatant with lots of intact phages
   b. Phage heads without the DNA
   c. Uninfected bacteria in the pellet
   d. Pellet with infected bacteria
   e. Both a and b are correct

3. Which enzyme catalyzes the removal of the RNA primer and synthesis of a DNA strand being made from the 5' to 3' direction in both leading and lagging strands?
   a. DNA polymerase I
   b. DNA polymerase II
   c. DNA polymerase III
   d. Topoisomerase
   e. Helicase

4. In an analysis of the nucleotide composition of DNA to see which bases are equivalent in concentration, which of the following would be true?
   a. A + C is same as A + T
   b. A = G and C = T only
   c. A + C = G + T only
   d. A + T = G + C
   e. All the above choices are possible.

5. The following are features of the structure of DNA **except**
   a. the strands of DNA are antiparallel.
   b. ribose-phosphate forms the backbone of DNA.
   c. the double helix is right- or left-handed.
   d. the nitrogenous bases are always on the outside.
   e. A base pairs with T and G base pairs with C.

6. Which enzyme makes the small RNA fragment to help initiate the DNA synthesized in the 5' to 3' direction?
   a. Primase
   b. DNA ligase
   c. DNA polymerase III
   d. Topoisomerase
   e. Helicase

7. Which enzyme connects the Okazaki fragments of a DNA strand being synthesized in the lagging strand?
   a. Primase   b. DNA ligase
   c. DNA polymerase III   d. Topoisomerase
   e. Helicase

8. The mistakes that happen during DNA replication are recognized and repaired by
a. endonuclease.
b. DNA ligase.
c. DNA polymerase III.
d. topoisomerase.
e. gyrase.

9. The shortening of telomeres is prevented by
a. exonuclease.
b. DNA ligase.
c. DNA polymerase III.
d. topoisomerase.
e. telomerase.

10. Fredrick Griffith observed the following experimental result to show how the transformation happened in *Streptococcus pneumoniae* bacteria.
a. R-strain caused the disease.
b. S-strain did not the disease.
c. Heat killed S-strain caused the disease.
d. Heat-killed S strain mixed with R-strain did cause the disease.
e. Heat-killed R strain mixed with S-strain did not cause the disease.

B. Short Answer Questions

1. Draw a conceptual diagram of DNA double helix showing five structural features such as 5' ends, 3' ends, A-T bonding, G-C bonding etc.

2. List six enzymes involved in DNA replication and their functions.

3. What are the three major mechanisms of DNA repair? Include the stages of cell cycle each of them occur in eukaryotic cell

D. Fill in the blanks

1. The complementary base pairing rules in DNA mean that _____ pairs with _____ and _____ pairs with _____.

2. DNA stores the genetic information in _____ and it is used as a template to make _____, which then goes to cytoplasm to make proteins.

3. The 5' and 3' end of a DNA strand refer to the _____ and _____ groups attached to the _____ and _____ carbons of the deoxyribose respectively

4. DNA replication is considered _____ as one of the DNA strands is used as the template to make a new strand of DNA based on _____ base-pairing rules.

5. The two modes of DNA repair are _____ repair and _____ repair.

Name _____

A. Multiple Choice Questions

1. The processing of a eukaryotic mRNA transcript involves
   a. the removal of exons and the splicing of introns.
   b. the addition of a guanine cap and a Poly A tail.
   c. the removal of introns and splicing of exons.
   d. Only a and b are correct.
   e. Only b and c are correct.

2. In eukaryotic cells, transcription happens in the
   a. ribosomes.   b. cytoplasm.   c. nucleus.
   d. cell wall.   e. cytoskeleton.

3. The following are directly needed for protein synthesis EXCEPT
   a. rRNA.   b. tRNA.   c.mRNA.   d. amino acids.
   e. DNA.

4. Protein synthesis happens in the
   a. nucleus.   b. cell membrane.   c. ribosomes.
   d. chromosomes.   e. cell wall.

5. What is the relationship among DNA, a gene, and a chromosome?
   a. A chromosome contains hundreds of genes which are composed of protein.
   b. A chromosome contains hundreds of genes which are composed of DNA.
   c. A gene contains hundreds of chromosomes which are composed of protein.
   d. A gene is composed of DNA, but there is no relationship to a chromosome.
   e. A gene contains hundreds of chromosomes which are composed of DNA.

6. Where is the attachment site for RNA polymerase?
   a. exon
   b. initiation region
   c. promoter region
   d. operator region
   e. intron

   Use the following choices to complete the sentences in 7 to 9. The choice may occur once, more than once or not at all.
   a. rRNA   b. tRNA   c. mRNA
   d. amino acids   e. DNA

7. Which one serves as an adapter between amino acids and the codons in mRNA?

8. The _____ carries the information to make specific proteins.

9. The _____ carries the information to make RNA.

10. The processing of proteins involves all the following EXCEPT
   a. the removal of transit peptide.
   b. the addition of oligosaccharide.
   c. the removal of amino terminus.
   d. zymogen activation.
   e. the removal of introns and splicing of exons.

B. Short Answer Questions

1. Draw the components of an eukaryotic gene with all essential components needed for transcription to occur.

2. Write the complementary strand of the given DNA sequence and then transcribe the DNA sequence below into an RNA strand (mark 5' and 3' orientation of mRNA) then translate that into an amino acid sequence using the codon table provided in the book.

   Promoter 5'-AAT TCC GTT GTC TAC GGA CAT GAT TAG GGT AGT GGG AAA TGA-3'

3.   List all the components involved in Transcription and their specific functions.

4.   What are the three major types of RNA and their specific roles in translation?

5. List two ways that fidelity (accuracy) of protein synthesis is maintained. Briefly explain the mechanism ensuring the fidelity in each case.

6. Transcription is initiated by the _____ factors which are _____ binding to the _____

   sequence on the DNA .

7. mRNA processing in eukaryotes includes the addition of _____ at 5' end and _____ at the 3' end of

   RNA, removal of _____ , and joining of _____

8. Codons are present in _____ and anticodons are present in _____ and both serve to _____

   _____

9. The information to make proteins is present in _____ carrying information from _____ to specify the

   amino acids which are attached to specific _____ , which come to ribosomes to make proteins.

10. The enzyme _____ attaches the right amino acid to the right tRNA based on

    its _____ .

11. Draw a flow chart starting with DNA showing transcription, RNA processing, transport to cytoplasm, translation and protein processing with conceptual figures to organize the materials from the chapter on transcription and translation in an eukaryotic cell.

Worksheet 11
Bacteria, Viruses, and Regulation of Gene Expression

Name _____

A. Multiple-Choice Questions

1. Viruses have some of the properties of living organisms. Which of the following is a characteristic of all organisms, **EXCEPT** viruses?
    a. Genetic information stored as nucleic acid
    b. Ability to control or program metabolism
    c. Ability to perform metabolic reactions
    d. Structure includes proteins and nucleic acid
    e. DNA may code for RNA and protein

3. Sexual mating of bacteria resulting in gene transfer is also known as
    a. transduction.
    b. transposition.
    c. conjugation.
    d. transformation.
    e. conjunction.

4. When lactose alone is present in bacterial medium, the lac operon is
    a. highly expressed.
    b. moderately expressed.
    c. not active at all.
    d. cAMP levels block the expression.
    e. It depends on tryptophan concentration.

5. When abundant tryptophan is present in the bacterial medium, the trp operon is
    a. highly expressed.
    b. moderately expressed.
    c. not active at all.
    d. It depends on mitosis of cells.
    e. It depends on lactose concentration.

6. The plasmid responsible for conjugation of bacteria is
    a. R.   b. F.   c. C.   d. B.   e. Z.

7. Which of the following is an example of long-term transcriptional control of gene expression in eukaryotes?
    a. DNA in older cells are more methylated than in younger cells.
    b. mRNA exists for a specific time before it is degraded.
    c. Phosphorylation of a protein makes it active.
    d. RNA processing occurs before mRNA exits the nucleus.
    e. A leucine zipper motif protein binds to an enhancer element.

8. Which of the following is a plausible mechanism proposed for coordinating the expression of multiple genes for enzymes in a biosynthetic pathway in eukaryotic cells?
    a. The genes are usually located on different chromosomes.
    b. The genes are all under the control of a single promoter.
    c. A regulator protein recognizes a specific cis-acting element in every gene.
    d. The genes are amplified and rearranged during the development of the cell.
    e. They are all pseudogenes which are expressed all the time.

9. Examples of transcription factors are
a. promoters and enhancers involved in gene regulation.
b. RNA polymerases binding to the promoter.
c. DNA polymerase binding to DNA.
d. primase and helicase involved in DNA replication.
e. HLH, Leucine zipper, and zinc finger proteins regulating transcription.

Use the following choices to answer questions 10 through 12.
a. long-term transcriptional regulation
b. posttranscriptional regulation
c. translational regulation
d. posttranslational modification
e. short-term transcriptional regulation

10. Rapid degradation of mRNA to stop gene expression is an example of _____.

11. Zymogen activation is an example of _____.

12. Storage of mRNA for the right timing before making proteins is an example of
_____

B. Short Answer Questions
Define the following terms and give one example of each.

1. Totipotency

2. . Gene expression

3. Coordinated gene expression

4. Transcription Factors

5. Tissue specific gene expression

6. Transposable element

C. Make a flow chart of regulation of gene expression at various levels in eukaryotic cells with specific examples.

Worksheet 12
Recombinant DNA Technology
Name _____

A. Multiple choice questions

1. DNA restriction fragments are size fractionated by _____
   a. filtering.
   b. centrifugation.
   c. gel electrophoresis.
   d. chromatography.
   e. electron microscopy.

2. What is a cloning vector?
   a. The enzyme that cuts DNA into restriction fragments
   b. A DNA probe used to locate a particular gene in the genome
   c. An autonomously replicating DNA fragment used to clone foreign DNA
   d. The laboratory apparatus used to isolate genes
   e. The sticky end of a DNA fragment

3. Which of the following statement best describes recombinant DNA technology?
   a. A set of techniques used to isolate DNA, characterize it, and transfer to other organisms
   b. Computer analysis of DNA and RNA sequence
   c. Genetic alteration of plants, animals and humans
   d. Introduction of pathogenic (disease causing) traits in to healthy organisms
   e. Gel electrophoresis and centrifugation.

   Use the following choices to answer questions 4 through 7. The answers may be used once, more than once, or not at all.

   a. Northern analysis
   b. RFLP analysis
   c. Western analysis
   d. PCR
   e. Gel electrophoresis

4. The gene expression at the mRNA level is revealed by _____.

5. DNA fingerprinting is performed through _____.

6. Which procedure will help detect the presence of protein in a sample?

7. The suspects in a crime can be sorted out by this technique.

8. The agency that sets the guidelines for scientists doing recombinant DNA research is the
   a. NIH.   b. FDA.   c. FBI.   d. CIA.   e. EPA.

9. The polymerase chain reaction is important because it allows us to
   a. insert eukaryotic genes into prokaryotic plasmids.
   b. incorporate genes into viruses.
   c. make DNA from RNA transcripts.
   d. make many copies of DNA.
   e. restrict eukaryotic genes.

10. The following is considered a potential misuse of genetic information from Human Genome project.
    a. Identifying genes responsible for diseases so as to find cures for them.
    b. Understanding the functions of 1000s of genes in human genome.
    c. Using the information to select people applying for jobs and insurance.
    d. Making diagnostic kits for genetic diseases.
    e. Using the information for genetic counseling.

C. Use the following terms to fill in the blanks.
These terms may be used once, more than once or not at all.

Agarose gel electrophoresis, Polyacrylamide gel electrophoresis, PCR, Restriction endonuclease, RFLP, Southern, Northern, Western, DNA library, vector, DNA ligase, Reverse transcriptase, DNA polymerase, *Agrobacterium tumefaciens, E. coli,* NIH, FDA, EPA, CIA, FBI, and USDA.

1. Technique used to study the expression of mRNA from a gene: _____.

2. Millions of copies of DNA can be made from a single copy by _____.

3. DNA or RNA can be size fractionated by this method _____.

4. Presence of a specific DNA in an organism can be verified by doing _____.

5. Genetically modified crops are regulated by _____.

6. The ecological impact of new recombinant technology is assessed by _____.

7. The presence of a particular protein is identified by using a labeled antibody in _____.

8. A collection of several DNA fragments cloned in plasmid or phage vectors is known as _____ _____.

9. The RNA-dependent DNA polymerase that makes DNA from RNA is _____

10. Proteins or DNA sequencing reactions can be size-fractionated on a _____.

11. An autonomously-replicating DNA vehicle that is used to clone and transfer DNA is known as _____.

12. The PCR reaction needs a thermostable _____.

13. Genetically altered foods are approved by _____, _____, and _____ before they can come to the market.

14. Restriction enzymes and _____ (enzymes) are needed to create a recombinant DNA molecule.

15. Suspects from a crime situation can be identified by _____.

16. The enzyme that can recognize a specific DNA sequence and cut the DNA in that site is called _____ _____.

17. The recombinant DNA safety guidelines are determined by _____.

18. DNA-RNA hybrids are used to detect gene expression in _____.

19. A small tissue sample is enough to make millions of copies of DNA by _____.

20. The bacteria commonly used to transform plants with genes from other sources are _____.